ADVANCE PRAISE

"Omer Bartov is the writer W.G. Sebald imagined himself to be."

—Joshua Cohen, author of the Pulitzer Prize winner
The Netanyahus

"As compelling as it is courageous, *The Butterfly and the Axe* is a remarkable work of creative historical excavation. Bartov stares straight into the horror of his family's wartime fate, and in imagining the deaths of those he never knew, rescues them from the mass graves and furnaces of history. It is a noble undertaking, but also an urgent and important one if future generations are to appreciate the tragic human reality behind those almost incomprehensible numbers."

—Bram Presser, author of *The Book of Dirt*, winner of the National Jewish Book Award

---

In this moving and imaginative novel, an Israeli woman says that she has spent her life "on the other side of [a] locked door." What lies beyond is her family's experience in the Holocaust, which remains a dark mystery to her, as it does for so many Jews today. As one of the world's leading historians of the Holocaust, Omer Bartov has spent a lifetime trying to illuminate that darkness, but in *The Butterfly and the Axe* he adds the tools of the storyteller to those of the scholar. Blending fact and fiction, he creates an unforgettable portrait of a few Jewish and Ukrainian lives during World War II. As Bartov writes, when the life of our ancestors is unimaginable, "we must imagine it. We cannot let them die as if they just vanished into thin air."

—Adam Kirsch, author of The Blessing and the Curse: The Jewish People and Their Books in the Twentieth Century

---

Omer Bartov's *The Butterfly and the Axe* is a novel of the Holocaust like no other. The novel takes us on a breathtaking journey into the hearts and minds of our contemporaries still deeply affected by the generational trauma of the Nazi genocide. Many voices speak in his stories, as Jews, Poles, and Ukrainians, descendants of victims and perpetrators, try to uncover the roots of memory and to make sense of history. Beautifully written and touchingly authentic, this is a book that will stay with you forever. Many novels have been written about the Holocaust. But if you want to read only one, read *The Butterfly and the Axe*.

—Elana Gomel, author of Little Sister and Black House

Eloquent and beautifully written, Omer Bartov's *The Butterfly and the Axe* is a poignant reminder of literature's capacity to fill in the voids of history. Equipped with the tools of a historian and the sensitivity of a gifted writer, Bartov's reconstruction of his family's past is a compelling narrative of the tragedy and richness of Jewish modernity.

—Amir Eshel, author of the poetry collection Between Deserts

We do not know how it really was, and yet we know, often more than is good for us. After so many novelists have tried to write history, it is fascinating to see what happens when a historian is impelled to write a novel.

—Leona Toker, author of Gulag Literature and the Literature of Nazi Camps

Is it possible to summon the voices of the murdered who vanished in the Holocaust? Can fiction fuse with family memoir to fill these gaps? In his novel *The Butterfly and the Axe*, Omer Bartov invents the archival record that answers this longing, documenting the betrayals and recovering the last days of the dead.

—Andrea Pitzer, author of *One Long Night: A Global History of Concentration Camps*

For those who think there are no Holocaust stories left to tell, Omer Bartov's astonishing and moving *The Butterfly and the Axe* proves this is not so. Combining the eye and ear of a novelist with the rigor of a historian, Bartov has fashioned something elegant and essential, restoring voice to the voiceless and honoring the lost through a vital act of imagination. Courageous, heartfelt, and true. I will not forget it.

—Mark Sarvas, American Book Award winning author of Memento Park and Harry, Revised

---

In *The Butterfly and the Axe*, Omer Bartov brings to life the tortured world of eastern Galicia—today's western Ukraine—during the Second World War, illustrating with nuance and feeling how compatriots of this once diverse region became victims and perpetrators of horrific violence. It simultaneously gives voice to the traumas of the Second World War and asks what we should do with them. A mesmerizing read.

—Megan Buskey, author of the forthcoming Ukraine Is Not Dead Yet: A Family Story of Exile and Return

THE BUTTERFLY
AND THE AXE

OMER BARTOV

ISBN 9789493276710 (ebook)

ISBN 9789493276697 (paperback)

ISBN 9789493276703 (hardcover)

Publisher: Amsterdam Publishers, The Netherlands

info@amsterdampublishers.com

The Butterfly and the Axe is part of the series **New Jewish Fiction**

Cover image: The watercolor on the cover is "Flowers and a Butterfly" by Dorit Weiser, Inv. No. 129.374, used by permission of the Jewish Museum in Prague.

CONTENTS

AUTHOR'S NOTE

This book contains autobiographical and historical elements but is ultimately a work of fiction. Its protagonists could have existed, however, and what happened to them is well within historical plausibility. My characters are intended to reimagine and bring back those who were eradicated and expunged from the historical record. Indicating where the line between truth and fiction lies is difficult, if not impossible, because in certain cases there may be more truth in fiction than in the mere retelling of facts.

PREFACE

I began thinking about this story some three decades ago, when my mother told me about the death of her great-grandfather in Galicia on the eve of World War II. At the age of 97 (or 103 depending on the version of the story), he waited for the members of the family to arrive from near and far to bid farewell before he died. Most of those who came were murdered shortly thereafter in the Holocaust, but no one ever found out the exact circumstances of their deaths.

Years later, when I was writing *Anatomy of a Genocide: The Life and Death of a Town Called Buczacz* (2018), I was struck by the fact that while I had spent 20 years researching this town, I ultimately had found nothing about how my own family members living there were murdered. I had recreated the life and death of a town going through thousands of documents and hundreds of testimonies, but my family had been eradicated and erased from the historical record, and there was nothing I could do about it. Yet I felt that I needed to do so in another way. Through my imagination, I needed to provide them with a credible life story, within the contours of history.

Over the years I also became increasingly aware that even if I, like so many others across several generations, did not know how my own family had been murdered, that unrecorded event had nevertheless traveled from one generation to another; an unspoken, inexpressible trauma that altered and damaged our psyches. It appeared to me that not only was it necessary to give justice to those who had been killed by imagining their lives and deaths rather than simply noting that they had occurred, but also that the long-term ramifications of this violence, the trauma that seeped from one generation to another, could only be mitigated by returning to the scene of the crime.

This book is an attempt to do so. It is therefore neither a work of fiction nor of history, neither a biography nor a conventional novel. It is an attempt to fill in the gaps that the historical record has left us to grapple with in ways that respect and conform to information we have yet transgress the limits of scholarship. It does so by presenting a series of characters who never existed, but could have; by linking actual, historical figures to imaginary ones; and by reconstructing the lives and deaths of actual people in a manner that cannot be supported by documents but emanates from the little that we do know about them from fragments of stories, rumors, and memories.

Because we can never return to the past, and because the past is always experienced and remembered differently by those who populated it, this book tells its story through the perspectives of real and imaginary characters. As a result, when we eventually discover what "actually happened," we are left to speculate whether it is the whole truth. The historical truth necessarily lies somewhere in-between, never quite resolved, and always disputed. In this journey into the past, we learn how one violent event, the murder of a family in a remote Ukrainian village in the spring of 1944, determined the fate of two families, one Ukrainian and one Jewish, in ways that could not easily be understood by later generations. At the same time, we see how that painful journey into the past, the obsession with finding out what happened, can bring about a modicum of peace and reconciliation. Thus we can take the bitter fruits of that violence and make understanding possible where previously there was denial, and replace hatred with love.

Straddling history and fiction, this book acknowledges that historical study as we know it cannot do sufficient justice to those who vanished without a trace. They need to be brought back so as to make history whole. Still, every letter, diary, and testimony reproduced within these pages closely follows a historical source. In that sense, the reader is left wondering, what is real and what is fiction? By breaking down the walls of the past, readers can enter a world that was once as real as our own, though it has now largely disappeared from memory and history.

For me, as an author, as a historian, it is important to keep the ambivalence created by the impossibility of distinguishing between what is fact and what is fiction. What I have written is meant to challenge both genres, and also my readers. Even if the past can only be reconstructed by imaginary characters within a historical framework, it does not mean that the narrative of this retelling is less true than an erratic documentary record that gives no voice to many of the victims of this era. There is no single historical truth, after all.

FAMILY TREES

THE SZUMER FAMILY
from the village of Mierzyn (Polish)—Myryn (Ukrainian)
moved to
Zakłócenie (Polish)—Zaklots (Yiddish)—Porushennya (Ukrainian)
Eastern Galicia, Poland

Old Szumer & his wife ———————————————————— Old Szumer's brother & his wife

Yitzhak (Izi)

Yakov
married **Renczi Berman**

Adolf
married **Tova**

Rochaleh
married **Max Reichert**

Two sons & a **daughter**

Hannaleh

Judit & David

Narrator

Tali

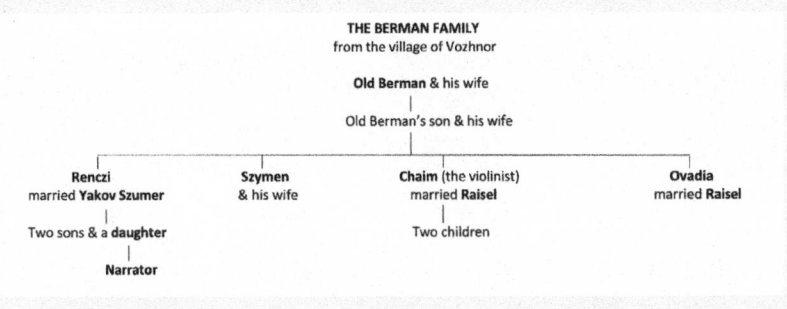

THE BERMAN FAMILY
from the village of Vozhnor

Old Berman & his wife

Old Berman's son & his wife

Renczi
married **Yakov Szumer**

Szymen
& his wife

Chaim (the violinist)
married **Raisel**

Ovadia
married **Raisel**

Two sons & a **daughter**

Two children

Narrator

THE KONOVALETS FAMILY
from the village of Mierzyn (Polish)—Myryn (Ukrainian)
moved to
Gloucester, Gloucestershire, UK

Grandfather **Mykhailo**
married **Yana**
|
Taras
married **Olga Orionova**
|
Andriy

THE GRAFINA'S FAMILY
From the village of Mierzyn (Polish) – Myryn (Ukrainian)

The Grafina

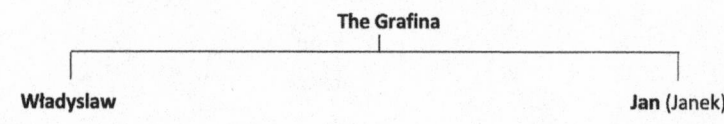

Władyslaw   **Jan** (Janek)

The Grafina's New estate manager **Dmytro Dowbusz**, his wife **Oksana**, and their twins

So many died in the great conflagration, so many vanished without a trace, their names unrecorded, their faces unrecognized, their stories dead and buried. No one will remember, no one will know. And yet, they still hover, just at the edge of consciousness, like ghosts that have never been put to rest. Then one day, as the last who might have known slip out of this world, they reemerge from oblivion and alter everything we thought we knew about our lives.

HELP ME GET ON THE RAILS

In early December 2016, my father's wife called me to say that his condition had deteriorated. If I still wanted to see him, it was time for me to come. The semester was coming to an end, and I informed my students that I'd be missing the last class. I managed to secure airline tickets for December 6, flying via London and arriving in Israel the following day. I had been travelling this route, often three times a year, for decades, and packing a carry-on suitcase for the planned two-week stay took little thinking. In the taxi to the airport, I was still responding to various work-related messages. It was a cool afternoon, the sun barely managing to peek out from behind the clouds, casting a few desultory rays on the brick facades on either side of the highway cutting its way across the city. Only after I had boarded the plane, found my seat, and turned off my phone did I begin to think about the purpose of my journey.

We took off in the dark. For a few moments I could see the lights of the city below as the plane headed toward the ocean. Then we crossed a band of clouds and were nothing more than a softly lit tube hurtling through the darkness. I had been planning a eulogy for my father for some time, although I had not told anyone. His

1

approaching demise was not much of a surprise. He had just turned 90, his health had been poor for years, and we all knew that it was only matter of time. But his mind had remained remarkably clear, and our weekly conversations on the telephone since I left the country almost 30 years earlier had lost none of their vigor. They did not betray the physical decay I observed with a mixture of compassion and abhorrence whenever we met. I suspected that this time he would actually die but could not quite imagine how it would play out. It had been two decades since my mother's death. I recalled how I choked on the phone when I called my wife on the way to the hospital after my father informed me that she had gone. What would it be like this time?

I completed my draft for the eulogy before dinner was served. I had it all planned out but writing a eulogy for a living person did not feel right. My father and I had a difficult relationship that I could only hint at in this kind of address. He was a public figure in Israel, and I did not want my private recollections and feelings to become grist to the mill for whichever journalists might be at the cemetery. In any case, he was still alive. The airhostess, a young, thin blond with a distinct Scottish accent, offered me wine. We always got along better on the phone than face-to-face, I thought. That was the gist of the eulogy. But what did it mean to say this? Why did an invisible barrier form between us as soon as we sat down to talk? What was it that remained unexposed during those long, often tense exchanges about everything else under the sun? It had been a long day. I took a sip of wine and dozed off.

Stepping off the plane the following afternoon at Ben Gurion Airport I was, as always, surprised by the blast of warm, humid air that greeted me as I descended the stairs and walked to the bus. All those years of flying back and forth from North America to the Middle East as I, too, grew older, more established, more distant from the land of my birth, that first encounter with it on the tarmac, that brief moment before being swallowed by the airconditioned bus, terminal, taxi, hotel, had always retained a certain quality I could never quite define. It is like the smell of a person you have not seen for ages suddenly floating past you on the street, evoking the image of a face, the sound of a voice, the feel of an embrace.

In the taxi I turned on my phone and began making calls. I'd meet my son for dinner that evening. My father was stable. I'd come to his house the following morning. The driver, his Hebrew betraying his Russian origins, wanted to make conversation. He mentioned that his two daughters speak Russian at home, and also read it. Russian is a language of culture. Israel doesn't have much of that. He also knew several Caucasian languages. He told me that he used to work for the army but that he makes better money as a taxi driver and gets to meet interesting people, like me. "It's hard to make a living here," he said. President Putin may be an authoritarian, but he brought order and a good economy. Here, it's just chaos.

The new forest of towers that had recently sprouted in Tel Aviv enveloped us as we entered the city. In my childhood, there was only one tall building in Tel Aviv, the Shalom Tower, and I recall watching from my window as a long plume of smoke rose toward the sky after it caught fire in the early 1970s. At that time, it was the tallest building in the Middle East. The fire was put out and the tower survived, but now it was obscured by all those new, gleaming structures, stretching their necks to command the best view of the Mediterranean to the West. We stopped at my hotel, situated in a refurbished Bauhaus building, for many decades the home of a well-known Israeli daily, on a narrow old Tel Aviv street.

3

"*Do svidania,*" I said.

Whenever we returned from our numerous trips abroad, my paternal grandfather, who never left the country after arriving in Mandatory Palestine in 1925, always greeted us at the airport as if we had just arrived in the Promised Land for the very first time. The young man at the hotel desk welcomed me with the effortless artificial politeness that had taken over businesses in Israel, which my father detested and I found somewhat amusing. "Welcome back," he said. "May I offer you a glass of wine?"

I arrived at my father's apartment in the late morning the following day. Having had a night's sleep, I thought I would be better prepared for the encounter. During breakfast at the hotel, I had noticed a middle-aged American holding a series of meetings with young Israelis, apparently recruiting high-tech talent fresh from their army service. Irritated by this business chatter as I tried to focus on my reading, I could not help admiring the man's gentle yet probing manner. The following year, when I was staying at the same hotel, I heard that the American had been killed in a bizarre accident, hit by a car that swerved off the road while he was sitting at an outdoor café. He was, I was told, a dedicated promoter of smart young Israelis. What skills these Israeli military graduates had acquired during their service, and what they would be used for in their new assignments, was left unmentioned.

Walking into my parents' home was always a journey back in time, no matter how often I had visited since leaving for my army service in the early 1970s. Not much had changed there. This became clear later on when I was looking through old family photo albums during my father's shiva. This tradition must have been established in middle-class Jewish families when photographs became the appropriate medium for preserving the memory of family members from childhood to old age. But my family's albums lacked labels, with the result that many faces looking out at me from the interwar years could no longer be identified, even though their features betrayed some family resemblance. My father was the last who could name them, and it was his death that had brought me to this gathering in the first place, where I was flipping through the thick pages of the albums with their glued little square black-and-white images. The sofa and armchairs, purchased during our two-year stay in London half a century ago, were still upholstered in the flowery pattern my mother had chosen at the time. I had found it quite garish in my teens but had gradually grown used to it, especially as it faded from the afternoon sun streaming through the wide windows facing West. Being on the seventh floor, we had once been able to see a good stretch of the sea. One wall of my parents' sitting room was covered with bookshelves, evenly divided between my mother's collection of books on psychology and psychoanalysis, my father's own publications, and works of fiction and poetry dedicated to them, at times with lengthy inscriptions, by the authors. One shelf, which had grown increasingly crowded over the years, contained my own books. On the opposite wall were several paintings, mostly by friends of my parents, frequenters of what had once been a kind of literary salon, where writers, poets, painters, architects, and a smattering of journalists, by now almost all dead, would gather. They would eat my mother's cakes, smoke, drink, argue about politics, gossip, and occasionally speak about their own work or even declaim some poetry.

That morning, my father was sitting on what looked like a remarkably uncomfortable armchair I had not seen before. His wife explained that it was intended to make it easier for him to sit down and get up. A bag of urine was hanging from a hook on the side, its tube disappearing under the blanket that covered his knees. His face had become very thin, and his large ears stood out. His eyes were a little moist and red and appeared much larger than I recalled them. He looked at me curiously, then recognized me. His voice had changed into a high squeak, and I could not quite understand what he was saying. I walked up to him and put my hand on his shoulder. It felt as if there was no flesh or muscle under his skin, just bare bone. He looked up at me and his expression was almost like that of a child, a faint, inquisitive smile. For the first time that I could remember my father was unable to speak, at least coherently; his gaze was confused, and a drop was suspended from the tip of his nose, which his wife quickly wiped. I had no idea what to do next.

"He is doing speech therapy," his wife said. "There is a young woman who comes in every day and helps him regain his words. He likes her. She is very pretty and nice. Maybe she even knows her business. The doctor says he will be better in a few days. He may have had a mild stroke. Would you like to drink something? Father and you always have a drink together. I bought a bottle of cognac especially for you."

Over the next few days his condition did improve. My sister's arrival from Europe cheered him up so much that he insisted on us gathering around his bed and raising a glass to celebrate this rare family reunion. We stood there, my sister, my niece, my father's wife, and myself. My father said, "Blessed are you our Lord, our God, King of the universe, who has given us life, sustained us, and brought us to this day."

The next day my sister decided to go back to her job, and I too worried that if the situation remained stable, I might have to return to North America. Then things took a turn for the worse. One day my father was trying to describe to me how beautiful, smart, kind, and caring his speech therapist was, painfully demonstrating his ability to pronounce difficult words, words that his therapist, he said, did not even know existed, and the next day he had relapsed into a fog of quasi-consciousness and inarticulate squeaks. It was heart-wrenching and infuriating at the same time. I recalled that when my mother was dying of cancer, and then fell and broke her hip in the hospital, she was administered just enough morphine to dull the pain but not enough to render her unconscious. As a result, she began raving and raging, especially at my father, who sat there helplessly, not shouting back at her as he had done so often in the past. He could not really defend himself in any case, as much of what she said in her delirium was true. They had removed her false teeth and it was hard to understand her speech. She had been a proud and dignified woman, though always resentful, and the other people in the ward looked up to her. Now she had reverted to some other side of herself, one which she would have never wanted others to see. I asked the doctor to help protect her from this last humiliation, and he protested that his hospital did not engage in euthanasia. But the next day he did discreetly raise the dose, and she passed away peacefully not long thereafter. My father was sitting quietly next to her as I made him lunch in the same apartment in which he was now dying. Then he called to tell me that she was gone.

Now it was my father's turn to no longer be himself, that self which was always a voice, an opinion, an argument, and especially a story, a story to illustrate and make a point, to dramatize and to mock, or simply to fill the silences that he abhorred, to fill the air with words that meant life was continuing as long as the story had not come to an end or another did not follow in quick succession. Now all he could muster was a squeak or pleading gaze. He appeared like a toddler in distress, not yet able to articulate what it needs. It was hard to endure. I kept myself busy, meeting friends, going for walks along the seafront.

One evening I set out from my father's apartment, located in a row of several ten-story buildings, to which we had moved in 1970, shortly after it was built. I walked toward the neighborhood of my early childhood, built in the first two decades after the establishment of the state to accommodate immigrants from Eastern Europe. The area was mostly made up of two or three-story houses with small apartments surrounded by lawns and trees, although my family had lived on the sixth floor of the only eight-story structure that neighborhood. It was a two-bedroom apartment, so my parents slept on a foldout sofa in the sitting room.

I remembered playing outside in the afternoons until our mothers would summon us home for dinner. Standing on the porches, they would call our names in Polish-accented Hebrew or whistle their family's distinct tune. Now most of the residents were elderly people. The remnants of the Arab village that until 1948 had been perched on a hill overlooking the sea, where we used to play cops and robbers, had mostly disappeared. It had been taken over by the dorms of the ever-expanding university, a somewhat sinister-looking state security building, and a museum celebrating a pre-state paramilitary organization. I strolled through dark backyards, intermittently lit by flashes from televisions in people's sitting rooms. The scent of the vegetation took me back to those early days when I would come back home with scraped knees, wolf down my supper of egg and salad and cheese and bread, and go to sleep to the sound of my father's typewriter and the smell of cigarette smoke wafting from his study.

My father did not keep me waiting long. I managed to squeeze into my two-week visit not only the last days of his life and the longer than usual wait for the funeral, but also the first four days of the Shiva. On the morning of his death, as my Google Calendar reminds me, I was still busy trying to renew my ancient Israeli driver's license. I took a taxi to his house around lunchtime. His wife had made him some soup, and he insisted on eating in the kitchen. We took him there from the bedroom, his Filipina maid securing the catheter tube to prevent it from getting entangled in the wheelchair. He ate a few spoonfuls and we took him back to his special armchair, which I recall thinking of as a device transported from Kafka's penal colony.

A few moments later he asked to go back to bed. I had a distinct feeling that life was draining out of him. At that point my niece showed up—young, energetic, and experienced with the dead and the dying from years of work in some of the world's most wretched countries. We were all standing around him in the tiny bedroom, by the small double bed in which my parents had slept until my mother's death, and where he now slept with his second wife. His eyes lit up for a moment when he spotted his granddaughter. She spoke to him in a light tone. I could not speak at all. I think he wanted me to touch his hand, so I did. He was clearly dying, and I had no idea what to say. Then, as if he had seen something none of us could observe, he said quite clearly, "Why don't you help me? Why can't you help me get on the rails?"

"What are you talking about?" His wife asked.

My niece climbed into his bed, lay down next to him, and held him. He breathed for another moment or two, now less tense. Then I could hear his last breath escape from his lips. She had helped him on to the rails.

THE CHILDREN'S HOUSE

The next few hours were a surreal blur. Since my father had died at home, the police had to be called. Two officers showed up, a trim young man and an older, overweight woman. I assured them that no foul play was involved. The younger officer inquired after my profession and was thrilled to hear that I was teaching a course on genocide. "My girlfriend is studying genocide at the Open University," he said. "She will be so excited to hear that I met an expert."

The other officer asked, "Are you the son of the writer?"

I said that I was.

"My husband and I recently retired," she said, "and I decided to volunteer with the police. We had to scale down a bit and gave away most of our books. Those we have read we don't need anymore, and those we haven't read we probably won't have time to read. But my husband loved your father's books, so we have kept them."

I thought to myself that I would never have such a conversation with police officers where I now lived. After this exchange, the investigation was swiftly wrapped up.

When my mother died, the only official procedure for burial in Israel was through the religious authorities. But my mother, who came from an Orthodox background, had developed a visceral hatred for the Jewish religious establishment in Israel. She wanted a secular burial, and my parents purchased a plot in the small cemetery of the kibbutz where they had lived for a few years following their studies at the Hebrew University. They had begun attending the university after my father was released from the British Army in 1946, but their studies were then interrupted by the 1948 War. I was born in that kibbutz shortly after they moved there.

In the late 1990s, arranging my mother's burial had been a major undertaking. When the truck from the kibbutz arrived at the mortuary, my father and I had to take my mother's body out of the fridge, lift it onto a cart, and roll it up a slope to where the truck was waiting with a pinewood coffin on its cargo bed. Holding my mother's damp, cold, and surprisingly heavy body was, I thought, the kind of experience that our modern Western societies have done everything to protect us from. What my father felt, I cannot say. But his fraught relationship with my mother ended only after his own death two decades later, and even then, it remained inscribed in his writings, which is where I will leave it.

By the time my father died, private burial services had become common in Israel for those who could afford them. The professionals that my nephew had called were soon on the scene, removing my father's body from the apartment as soon as the police had completed their report. Now all that remained was to formulate a formal announcement of his death and to respond to any resulting queries from the press. "The journalist, lover of the land and the people of Israel, the author and Israel Prize laureate, has passed," it said. His death did not elicit much public interest.

A few days later, one of the TV channels broadcast a brief item on my father at the very end of the evening news. The era when intellectuals molded public opinion and sparked conversations in Israel had long passed, and my father had retired almost a quarter of a century earlier from his position as a columnist in a widely read newspaper. Because he had recently been awarded the Israel Prize at a state-sponsored event, we thought his passing ought to have elicited some form of official recognition. But the country in which he died was very different from the country for whose independence he had fought. Modern Israel has little interest in writers and intellectuals, especially those with a critical eye. My father never shied away from pronouncing his opinion whenever the media gave him the opportunity. Since the state showed no interest in his death, the funeral arrangements were simple to make.

Although my mother, and consequently my father, who wanted to be buried next to her, had rejected the idea of any posthumous contact with the religious authorities, the old Jewish tradition of burying the dead as soon as possible still prevailed. It certainly made sense business-wise for private burial services, eliminating the need for long-term storage. In my father's case, speedy burial was not possible since my sister had to return from Europe.

I spent most of that first day after his passing in my father's home. I had already had my share of loss and death. But like most people, I had little experience with funerals, let alone improvised affairs conducted outside the uniform pattern of Jewish religion, where much of the formal routine is handled by experienced, if jaded, Orthodox officials. Between answering calls from friends and family, I went over the draft of my eulogy. It did not seem to amount to much, I thought, but at least it was sincere.

We were very close, my father and I, and very far. We were also very similar. His legs looked exactly like mine when they protruded from his shorts. My voice sounded to others so much like his that during my youth, whenever I answered the phone in our family home I would always be mistaken for my father. The similarities made for distance. His affection increased with time and age, while mine became less needy and turned toward more of an expression of dutiful compassion for an old man. Yet almost until the very end he could make my blood boil as no one else besides my sister. His natural kindness was tightly bound by a set of unyielding ideological principles, more rigid, I think, than his own father's religious strictures, because, perhaps, of his abrupt departure from the fold when he joined the army at the age of 17. As for my own tolerance for a wider range of opinion, I eventually came to perceive it as a facade covering my need for a carefully preserved distance even from those closest to me and my embarrassment and impatience with displays of emotion. This has always made for a degree of bewilderment and helplessness in the face of outpourings of grief, as well as love. Only rage appears to me somewhat less indecipherable.

I did not dwell on any of this in my eulogy. Perhaps this understanding, if anything still needs to be understood, has emerged only now, as I write these words. And so, I just typed the text on my father's computer and printed it. The only other remaining close family member was his younger brother, who had worn a skullcap years after my father had discarded his. We all agreed that a funeral in a kibbutz was perfectly appropriate, but just as in my mother's case two decades earlier, it seemed fitting that as the only son, I would recite the kaddish, the Jewish prayer for the departed. "In his will," my uncle said on the phone, "Father asked that you recite the complete version." My uncle was very ill, and I was thankful that he was still willing to help with so much of the organization. As a former career officer in the military and a much more engaged family man than my father had ever been, he was far better suited to this role than me. I had distanced myself from the family and often disdained what I saw as meaningless gatherings of people who had little in common but their shared ancestry. But I did love my uncle dearly and always thought of him as a gentler, more empathetic version of my father.

An old poet friend of my father's called that afternoon. Well into his nineties, he sounded tearful. I remembered him as a gruff domineering figure, inseparable from his pipe and with the air of a French existentialist incongruously grafted onto his well-maintained sabra exterior and untroubled nationalism. As I spoke with him, my thoughts wandered to some lines by a younger and better poet, remembered from my school days: "I can only tell my own story, my world is as narrow as that of an ant." The old poet asked to speak at the funeral. He and my father were ancient friends and rivals. My father's wife said, "Father asked that we do not to let him speak at his funeral. You know him, he always ends up speaking only about himself." I tried to persuade the poet that this would be a small family affair without long speeches. "I just want to read a poem I wrote for him," he countered. I could not refuse.

The next day I met my sister for breakfast at the hotel. From there we were to go to my father's apartment, and then to the kibbutz where the funeral would take place. Over the last few days, the weather had been glorious, as is often the case in December in Israel. I had to borrow some old t-shirts from the closet in my father's bedroom, because it was too warm for button-down shirts. I was quite sure that at least one of those items of clothing had belonged to my mother. My father had grown a sizeable paunch and wore a larger size, and in any case, I had never seen him in a t-shirt. He preferred real shirts or, in his later years, vests, of the kind that Marlon Brando had popularized when he could still show off his muscles.

That morning the sky was cloudy, and rain was forecast for the afternoon. My sister and I compared eulogies. She looked much older than I remembered. Over the years, we had grown distant. I did not like what she had written, thinking that she wore her emotions on her sleeve. She had loved my father as only a teenage girl can idolize a parent. Still, she had endless fights with him, which he would report to me in our weekly phone conversations. He longed to be reconciled with her but stood his ground like a petty tyrant defending the last crumbling bastion of his domain. She wanted him all to herself, but first my mother stood in the way, then his second wife. There was no way forward, not even after death. We exchanged some polite words and parted. "I love Israeli breakfasts," she said. Like me, she had been living out of the country for decades.

By the time I reached the kibbutz, less than an hour's drive north of Tel Aviv, the weather had turned cooler, and a few raindrops were falling. Turning off from the highway, I passed several agricultural settlements that still resembled the kibbutzim I recalled from my youth, when going to what we called labor camp—without any allusion to World War II—was all the rage. I recalled the joy of escaping the narrow confines of our homes and the unavoidably close proximity to our parents to spend weeks working in the fields and sleeping without supervision in a mixed company of boys and girls.

My parents left the kibbutz for Tel Aviv soon after my birth. I have no memory of the first 18 months of my childhood, which I spent in a children's home rather than with my parents, as was the norm at the time in these socialist communities, since the family was considered an obstacle to communal harmony and solidarity. The cluster of kibbutzim in that valley was founded in the early years of Mandatory

Palestine, and those who remained nostalgic for the austere and idealistic beginnings of Jewish settlement on the land described them as a remnant of old Eretz Israel. Memories are selective. Before the War of 1948, several Arab villages were situated in that same valley. But they were not part of that nostalgia and no one I have spoken with has ever mentioned them, apart from an old Palestinian who showed me a map from the period with these villages clearly marked.

I parked not far from the cemetery and made my way toward the small crowd that had already gathered there. Some of my friends had come. We had known each other since high school or our army service, well over four decades earlier. They had all been to my home and had known my parents in their prime, as I had known theirs. This was the end of the road. My friends and I were now much older than our parents had been when we first met. My former wife was there. She lived not far from my father and had grown close to him in recent years. Her parents, both deceased, had been to university with mine. As we walked together to the site of the grave, I recognized many of the names carved on the tombstones, although I had met only a few of them. They were all born elsewhere, mostly in Poland and Belgium. But we spoke of them as the salt of the earth, the founding generation. Compared to them, we were just one more step in the ongoing realization of the dream. But just like the kibbutz, the dream had been privatized and we had gone on our separate paths.

Someone was urgently calling my name. The ambulance had arrived with my father's body, and I was asked to identify him. I climbed into the vehicle and the nurse uncovered his face. "Yes, it's him," I quickly confirmed. But in fact, it did not look like my father at all. It was a corpse. No effort had been made to care for his appearance. After all, he would soon be dumped into a grave. Ashes to ashes, dust to dust, I thought, and rejoined my friends. A few family members and friends of my parents were also there: my uncle, my sister, my father's wife, the old poet. We gathered around the hole in the ground. It looked like it would rain at any moment, and the wind was picking up. "We better get on with it," said my uncle. He looked frail and in pain. He is not long for this world, I thought, already mourning him. It was easier to mourn him, even though he was still alive, than my father, who was now just a corpse wrapped in a shroud about to be lowered into the ground. My uncle was my favorite member of the family. I read the kaddish in my halting Aramaic. When I was done my uncle leaned over to me and whispered, "Father asked for the complete version." I did not know the difference then and still don't, but had obviously again, for one final time, failed to do what my father had requested. No one noticed. A friend sang the prayer, "God full of mercy." Then I read my little speech about communicating with my father from a distance, and how I would now miss those weekly conversations, in which we used to speak about everything but the love between a father and a son. "In his last moments," I said, "he told us that for him God was not a figure that resides outside of man but within him. There are people who have God within them and those who do not have God within them." My father always sought God in his fellow man. When he found Him, he embraced them with all his heart. About the others, after all, there is little to say.

My sister made her speech about loving my father despite it all. How will she keep living now that he is gone? I wondered. Then the old poet read his poem. "All our exploits and heroisms," it began, listing them one by one, "all the wounds we bequeathed to our sons and our grandsons," it went on, "all we destroyed with our own hands, without solace, and that peace we never had under our vine and our fig tree, and the time that keeps running out." It was a beautiful poem, and he said nothing else. Just then the rain began coming down. A few years later, I discovered that someone had posted a video of that reading on YouTube. Listening to it, I teared up.

I don't remember how the body was put into the grave. But on the way to the modest reception the kibbutz had arranged, in one of those plain one-story buildings that kibbutzim still seem to be made of, an old woman approached me. "I remember you from the children's

17

home," she said in a remarkably girlish voice. She showed me a photograph. "You were such a cute baby," she said, and I thought, that's what people say about all babies. And in any case, I did not appear particularly cute in that photo, munching on a biscuit and looking straight into the camera. But I took a picture of the photo just in case. In the background, one can still see the outline of the children's home. Later, I could not find any similar photo in the family albums. Was that actually me? Why was that old woman carrying my photo in her purse?

We stood around for a while at the reception. There was hot water for making coffee or tea, plastic cups and paper plates, some fruit, cakes, and light drinks. I cannot recall if there was any wine. People made small talk. It was a good opportunity to catch up with old friends, but impossible to have a meaningful conversation. After a while, I left. That's it, I thought to myself. But I'm not quite sure what I meant by that.

TALI

When my mother died, the shiva at my parents' home was a lively social event, not least because of my father; many people passed through to express their condolences and to spend some time with him. Quite a few older women showed up, both to say how sorry they were about my mother's passing and to indicate their availability as a new spouse. Jewish tradition does not like leaving gaps where they can be filled. Men should not be alone, certainly not in old age. My father was in no condition to respond to these signals at the time, but he was in top form as a host and an entertainer. My sister and I loathed the whole event. We mostly sat in the kitchen with our friends, smoked, drank coffee or wine, and griped. In retrospect I feel sorry about missing some of the stories that were told by the old folks. I have no memory of what we talked about in the kitchen.

My father's shiva was more subdued. Everyone was older. Most members of his generation were already dead, and none of us could live up to his standard as a host. Even when he was very old and spent much of the day just staring at the TV or sleeping, he would perk up and become himself again whenever anyone walked into the room. Then he would tell stories, repeat old jokes, and complain about the political situation. When the guests left, he'd slump back in his armchair and doze off.

My sister left two days after the funeral, and I left soon after her. The weather had cleared up and I tried to take some walks along the beach when I didn't have to be at the shiva. As I half listened to the conversations around me, I occupied myself with looking through the photo albums that my father's wife brought out from his study. The farther I went back in time, the fewer faces I would recognize. I wished there was still someone left to ask about the identity of the people posing for the camera. None of the visitors had any clue.

I made small talk with strangers who introduced themselves to me, embarrassed to admit that I did not even know whether they were family members or friends of my father. I made a lot of coffee and tea. The day before I flew back, I found myself speaking with a woman I was sure I had never met before, even though she did turn out to be a relative. In her late forties or early fifties, she had striking deep blue, almost purple eyes. Her short black hair was streaked with some gray, and her narrow, tanned face was marked by distinctive wrinkles, some of which, especially at the corners of her eyes, appeared to signal laughter, and others, mostly around her mouth, suggesting pain. She walked in wearing a leather jacket and dark pants, a slim, slight woman in high boots. After looking around the room for a moment, she sat down next to me on the sofa, pulled off her boots, and folded her legs under her.

"Tali," she said, stretching out her hand. "I'm sorry for your loss. My mother knew your father quite well." She must have been strikingly beautiful as little as ten years ago, I thought. She worked in a travel agency and had travelled around the world, she told me.

"I also travel a lot," I responded, "but mostly in Europe."

"I believe you know Ukraine quite well, isn't that right?"

"As a matter of fact, I do," I answered, somewhat surprised, "but mostly its western parts, the area that used to be called Galicia."

"That's where our family comes from," she noted.

I poured her some tea. She took a sip and appeared to be mulling something over.

"Listen," she said, "can we meet at some point? I want to ask you about some things concerning our family. I had meant to ask your father, but now it's too late. And in any case, you may know more because of your profession."

I was still not sure how we were related. "I am leaving tomorrow morning, but maybe we can meet for dinner this evening. People usually leave the shiva by seven or eight."

———

"I went to Ukraine in 2003," Tali began.

We had just ordered some food and wine at a busy seaside restaurant. I was having second thoughts about this meeting. It was already 9 p.m. and I still had to pack in order to head to the airport early the next day. But I was also curious to hear what this woman I had just met had been doing in a part of the world that was of special interest to me.

"My grandmother and mother always spoke about the town in Galicia we come from, and I thought it was time for me to see it. I was going through a personal crisis at the time. I lost my grandmother when I was ten, and my mother, as your father may have told you, was never entirely stable mentally, and after the loss of her mother she progressively got worse and went in and out of mental institutions. Every time I visited her, she insisted that she absolutely had to go back to her hometown, that nothing here could cure her. She didn't belong to this place, only going back would bring her solace and peace. This was totally insane, of course, because my mother was born in Tel Aviv in the mid-1930s, and had been to Galicia only once, as a little girl just before the war. But she would have none of it, and kept repeating that she never belonged to Israel, that people here were cruel, and callous, and ignorant, that the climate did not agree with her, that she was always sweating and could not bear the constant humidity. She missed the green hills and streams and forests of her hometown, and the gentle, soft sound of the languages spoken there, the comforting melody of her parents' Yiddish. This was ironic, given that her parents always fought in Yiddish, thinking that she did not understand the horrible things they were saying to each other. Perhaps that was why she wanted to go back, because they made her life here so hateful. They stayed together for as long as they did only because of her, and she, in fact, was born only because they badly wanted to leave their hometown. Had they not left, they would not have been together—I can tell you more about that, if you like—and then she would not have been born, and she would have been spared all the suffering she endured all those years. And so would have I."

"So, your mother was Hannaleh," I said. "I remember my father speaking about her always wanting to go back. He could never understand. He would tell her, 'But Hannaleh, everyone was murdered. Why would you want to go back?' But she insisted."

"Yes," said Tali, "the fact that everyone was killed never seemed to sink in. Although there was one case she was obsessed with in her last years. I'll get to that later, too."

"So, she passed away?"

"Yes, in 2009. She was only 74. But it was better that way. Her mind was completely gone."

"My mother also died when she was 74," I said.

"I know. She was such an impressive woman. You must miss her."

"I do, sometimes. And you?"

"I have always been alone in the world, so, I don't really know what to miss. My grandmother was very unhappy. She detested my grandfather and had many lovers, which made her even more bitter. I don't think she ever quite knew what to do with my mother. My sense is that she took her along to those rendezvous because she could not leave the child alone in the house, but she also totally neglected her and was resentful about having to look after her.

"My grandfather was not really someone who could raise a child. He became increasingly morose, was then sick for many years and died young. So, you know, my mother had no idea what a family looks like, because she never really had one. She lived in a fantasy world that was entirely closed off to me. And when I was 11, I was sent to a kibbutz, as what they called an 'external child.' At the time they still had those educational institutions for kids from broken families. We were kept apart from the regular kibbutz children. There was just a group of us damaged kids who were obviously not up to par with the true products of the collective, and although some of us were later taken in by an 'adoptive family,' I was not, and didn't want to be. I had a mother, after all, but someone must have told her that I would be much happier in the kibbutz and get a decent education.

"I think they also wanted to hide me because I was something shameful. I'm not even sure your father knew I existed, which is perhaps why I couldn't pluck up enough courage to speak to him. You see, I never knew who my father was. I don't even know if my mother knew. She never mentioned anyone and never married, so I was something illicit that had to be put away somewhere where no questions would be asked.

"But a kibbutz can't really be your mother and father, it's just a bunch of people sharing work and food, it can't hug you or love you or put you to bed or sing you lullabies. It can only give you food and shelter and send you to work and will never really accept you because you are external and just a spoilt little city kid whose skin is too pale and delicate and who wants dolls and nice clothes and likes to crawl into bed with a big old book and read late into the night.

"So now you know I never had a father and was taken away from my mother when I was 11 and that my existence was kept secret from the rest of the family because of the shame. I came to the kibbutz with two books that I think had passed on to my mother from my grandmother. They were not considered age-appropriate in the kibbutz, but I guarded them as my most precious possessions and read and reread them many times. Probably mostly because the kibbutz disapproved.

"One was *By Fire and Sword*. You must remember the old Hebrew translation of that novel by Sienkiewicz about the great Cossack uprising against the Poles. It was so romantic and tragic that I could just immerse myself in it and forget about having to work in the field pulling out weeds and being bullied by all those tanned and tough kibbutz kids. Instead I dreamt about handsome Polish noblemen in their armor and flamboyant Cossack warriors on beautiful steeds and the pale-faced princesses over whom they fought on the green fields of Ukraine.

"The other book, strangely enough, was *The Plague* by Camus, which even then I read as a warning of how a virus can penetrate a society and undermine it from within. Maybe sometimes I thought about myself as that virus, which was why I had to be hidden away in the kibbutz before I caused more damage to the family. At other times I thought of myself as the brave doctor who fights against the virus and saves his town, because I, like him, recognized that there was such a virus even as everyone else denied it; the virus that caused little girls to be removed from their mothers and put away in kibbutz institutions, and I would fight it to the bitter end even if eventually it would kill me.

"I learned how to fend for myself. It was hard and I was very alone and confused in that place of communal bliss. I remember that my literature teacher told me, maybe I was 16 at the time, that I was very smart, that I showed so much insight in my essay. I can't remember what I was writing about, maybe it was *Crime and Punishment*. I was so filled with joy that someone had complimented me not on doing a good job in the garden or keeping my tiny little closet tidy but on something I had written. I thought, this is what I want to do for the rest of my life. That teacher invited me to his room a few times to read some stories and poems together, but one evening he started touching me and I ran away filled with shame and horror.

"I was so afraid that I would be like my mother and grandmother that for months I could not read anything and started skipping classes, which no one really cared about in the kibbutz anyway. I thought I was worth absolutely nothing, that all the praise I had received from this man I had admired was a lie, that all he had wanted was to sleep with me. I think I actually had depression but in the kibbutz such terms were not really common. Finally, I could go to the army. After that, I never returned to the kibbutz.

"I hope you don't mind me telling you all this," Tali finished. "I don't even know why, this was not the reason I wanted to meet you, and here I am wasting your time with my little childhood traumas."

"How did you end up working in a travel agency?"

"That's another story," she said. "This was not my dream job when I left the army, even though now I think it was the best thing that could have happened to me. I wanted to study at the university. I moved in with a friend from the army to a tiny apartment in Ramat Aviv and started studying literature at Tel Aviv University. Looking back, I think those were the best years of my life, I just enjoyed every minute.

"I should tell you that it was also at that time that I read some of your father's writings and realized that he too had taught external children in the kibbutz where you were born. Even then I thought that I should contact him and tell him who I was, but I also knew that the children he taught were very different. Those kids came from the Holocaust, they were survivors of something horrible and horribly important for the Jewish people. I was just the neglected daughter of a deranged woman who didn't even know who her father was. So, in the hierarchy of pain and suffering I really had no right to compare myself with those children. At that point I decided never to speak or complain about those seven miserable years in the kibbutz. Besides, I was among the last to be sent to these institutions, which don't exist anymore. And so, I never contacted you father.

"In any case, my years at the university were utter bliss, especially the first three, doing my bachelor's degree. Everything I read was a new revelation, every lecture was eye-opening, every paper a journey of discovery and creativity. I had so much to learn and so much to say. During all those years of repression and silence, under the rough and dry surface of my skin, something had been simmering, ready to boil over just as soon as I took off the lid and turned the flame higher. And then, there I was, sailing from classroom to library, literally brimming with joy.

"After I completed my degree summa cum laude, one of my most admired professors asked whether I would pursue a second degree under his supervision. He even managed to arrange for me a modest grant to support my studies. It was a dream come true, and for the first time in my life I could actually imagine myself doing what I had never allowed myself to dream of before—becoming an academic. This may sound mundane to you, but it was the Everest of my fantasies.

"'You are so smart and intelligent,' he said to me. 'And so unlike all the other students. You have original ideas and thoughts, you don't follow trends and you don't fear authority, you are the real genuine item.' I could barely breathe, no one had ever spoken to me like that before, let alone someone I looked up to. I am sure you know who it was, but I will not mention his name. He was truly one of the most influential scholars at the time, although by now his star has waned. Long story short, I spent another three years working on my master's degree, which took longer than I anticipated.

"To make ends meet, I began working part-time for a tourist agency. I started with menial tasks and then took on more responsibility when they realized that I was good at my job. But things did not work out as I had hoped. The professor was kind and appreciative, the courses were interesting, and I think I produced some good research papers. But things got complicated.

"I find it hard to talk about this and can't believe how stupid I was. I was young and naïve, and, well, I had never been loved, so when he professed his love to me, I did not put up much of a defense. I knew that he was married and had children. It was rumored that he had had many mistresses over the years, especially among his students. But I was certain that my case was different, that he really loved me, that he actually found me smart and intelligent, genuinely original, and so forth. I loved that he loved me, although whether I loved him is less clear to me today. I became his mistress, his office our bedroom, his desk our bed. His appreciation for my mind became his desire for my body. My dreams of becoming a professor blurred into a muddle of confusion, guilt, and self-doubt, which ultimately turned into disgust and rage.

"Just weeks before I was supposed to hand in my final paper I simply left and never looked back. I began working full-time at the agency and went on a long trip to Europe. When I came back, I wrote my first tourist guide, something quite different from the usual fare, replete with quotations from literature and poetry, unique photos I had collected, and recommendations for special cafés and bars. It sold quite well, which led me to travel more and publish more of these books, none of which I suppose you have ever read.

"My professor tried to contact me several times, but I never responded. Eventually there was a scandal with another student. Compromising photos and recordings were leaked. His wife left him and the university forced him to retire. I even felt sorry for him, until I realized what he had done to me and so many other young women whose self-confidence he had shattered and whose dreams he had left by the wayside. It took a decade of traveling for me to feel finally liberated from the poison that man had injected into my body.

"It was then that I decided to find out what all that was about, that world my mother had never ceased dreaming about. The world that made it impossible for her to be happy where she was. Or perhaps precisely the opposite, the place that enabled her to go on living simply by imagining it as a better, still existing alternative—those dense forests, the rolling green hills, the cool clear water—that hometown in the valley. But it was not all fantasy, not only a figment of her imagination, because there still was that story she always told me about the visit to Galicia just before the war, and it was that story that I wanted to know more about, or that perhaps served as an excuse to describe this trip as having a practical side rather than being nothing more than an escape into my mother's hallucinatory universe. So that was why I went. But I knew so little and discovered more than I would ever want to know. It could last me a lifetime. On the other hand," Tali smiled, and for a moment her face looked almost youthful, "I also discovered love."

She was still wearing the same leather jacket but had put on a different blouse, and a necklace made of amber of the kind sold all over Poland and Ukraine. My mother had worn something similar, but not as delicate. Tali's blue eyes were fixed on me so intensely that my chest contracted. I finally realized that she was my great uncle's granddaughter.

Family genealogy had never been my strong suit. Adolf was my maternal grandfather's younger brother. He came to Palestine in the early 1930s, not as a Zionist but as a communist, with the Polish police hot on his heels. How strange to have met his granddaughter so late in life. My father had never mentioned that Hannaleh had a daughter. He probably didn't know she existed. He always spoke of Hannaleh kindly, but also a little dismissively, as one would of a child. She called him occasionally, just to tell him about her dream of returning to her hometown. "Not right in the head," he would mutter.

"What happened when you got to Ukraine?"

"Back then, not much more than a decade after the fall of the communists, it was not so simple to go there. I flew to Lviv, via Warsaw, and arranged to stay at the George Hotel in the center of the city. You must know the place. I arranged for a local to drive me around and serve as an interpreter. It was incredibly cheap, and even now I think it's not that expensive. I wasn't sure what I was looking for, apart from wanting to visit our fabled hometown.

"I needed to get away from everything in Israel. My crazy mom, another affair that was going nowhere, and a return of the PTSD I suffered during the first Gulf War, when the block I was living on was hit twice by Iraqi Scuds. After the second missile came down, I was convinced that they were after me. I was so shaken that I packed a few things and went to the desert, to the Ramon crater, for the rest of the war. Initially I was camping out, but the nights were so cold that I soon ended up in a youth hostel. The desert helped me readjust. Those vast boulders, the geological layers one on top of the other, compressed by weight and time. The mountaintops hurled to the valleys in ancient tremors, the immense stillness everywhere, the wind blowing through the scrub...

"I thought I had entirely gotten over my PTSD, but it returned with a vengeance when my mother was taken to the hospital again. Maybe it was never related to the rockets, maybe it was an older terror that I had never fully known or articulated, something I experienced or internalized as a child, a kind of generational dread that takes hold of you suddenly and won't let go.

"Landing in Lviv was like going back in time," Tali continued.

She had drunk a fair amount, but her meal was almost untouched, whereas I had finished eating. The restaurant was quieter now. Its lights were playing on the water, and you could hear the waves lapping against the dunes, and then rolling back into the darkness. In the distance Jaffa was lit up. A jetliner was coming in from the West, and I was reminded that my flight back to North America was only a few hours away.

"The airport," she said, "looked like an old bus terminal. It was one of those Soviet structures built for a different time, when planes were smaller, and no one had thought yet of walking straight out of the plane and into the terminal. It was March, and the air was cold as I disembarked and was instructed by a stern-looking official with a fur cap to board what looked like the kind of truck we used to travel in on school trips. Remember those? We'd always sing that stupid song on the way back, 'We're bringing peace upon you, we're bringing peace upon you, peace, peace, peace upon you!' All the parents would be waiting anxiously for their kids, the moms holding bags with sandwiches in case the children were hungry: 'You never know if they feed the children properly on those trips, they always look so thin when they come back.' Only my parents were never there. I told the other children that my father was killed in the war, that he fell for our country. I'd walk home on my own and find my mother in her bedroom with the blinds drawn. She would ask me to bring her some tea and see if there was any food in the fridge.

"Now when I think about it, this must have been just before I went to the kibbutz. Did I actually go on these trips at such a young age or am imagining it? Anyhow, unlike the trucks in Israel, those in Lviv airport were more like the top of a bus attached to a military vehicle. Ukraine is too cold for open trucks. Once we arrived at that puny terminal a gruff official asked me whether I had health insurance. At least I think that was what he asked; it was hard to tell as his accent was so thick. I cheerfully said that I did, and he let me through without asking for any proof, which was lucky as I had none. In the arrival area I spotted a tall young man holding a handwritten sign with my name on it in surprisingly well-formed Roman characters.

"'Miss Szumer?' he asked and reached for my bag.

"'Tali,' I answered, and we walked out of the terminal. There was still some snow in shaded areas and a cold blast of wind made me zip up my coat. He led me to a beat-up yellow car.

"'Welcome to independent Ukraine,' he said in a British accent. 'I will now take you to your hotel. My name is Andriy, Andriy Konovalets. But if you prefer, you can call me Andy.'

"We drove through the bleak suburbs of Lviv in Andriy's Russian-made Lada. He was a good driver and swung expertly around the numerous potholes. The heating was on full blast. Peeling off my coat gave me a chance to get a better look at him as I twisted around to put it on the back seat. He seemed to be in his early thirties, with longish, light-brown hair, green eyes, a snub nose, and a very fair complexion. Altogether rather handsome, I thought. The car smelled of gasoline and I rolled down the window to let in some air.

"'How come you speak such good English?' I asked.

"'Because I come from Britain,' he chuckled.

"'Oh, so you are not Ukrainian?'

"'I am, of course,' he responded, "but was born and raised in Britain. I only moved to Lviv a few months ago when I was offered this job at the travel agency. Are you tired or would you like to have something to eat after you check into the hotel? Lviv is a nice city with good food.'

"What a nice welcome, I thought to myself. We were now nearing the center of the city. It looked run-down, like other post-communist cities I had seen. It had once been an elegant town, more Central European than Russian.

"'Here we are,' Andriy suddenly announced, stopping the car next to a large, 19th-century building overlooking a large square. He accompanied me to the reception and made sure my room was ready. 'I'll fetch you for a walk and a dinner in about an hour,' he said and departed."

"You know," I said to Tali, looking around the empty restaurant, "I think we are the only people left here."

I suggested that we walk together to my hotel, and that I would call her a taxi from there. It had become a little chilly, but the sky was clear, and the air felt fresh and salty. "I must leave for the airport tomorrow morning at about seven," I said.

She laughed. "That leaves us plenty of time. As I found out," she went on, "Andriy's grandfather had come from Ukraine to England after the war, and ended up working on farms, I think in Gloucestershire. That night Andriy took me for dinner at a lovely little restaurant on a hill overlooking the city. I had Ukrainian borsht with sour cream, just like what my grandmother would make on those rare occasions when we sat together as a family, and *varenyky*, those Ukrainian pierogis, with wild mushrooms. We drank Georgian red wine."

As we made our way from the seaside into the city, Tali continued her story. "Andriy said his grandfather was always poor, and bitter. He had a wretched childhood in Ukraine. He came from a little village on the Dniester called Myryn, although at the time it was known as Mierzyn because this whole region belonged to Poland. He said that his family farm had nothing more than a couple of cows, three pigs, a few sheep, two dozen chickens, and just enough land to grow a few crops. He had six years of schooling before he was sent to work as a stableboy and farmhand at a nearby estate.

"Coming to Britain after the war didn't change much for Andriy's grandfather. There he did not even have land, but since his old farm would have been taken over by the communists in Ukraine anyway, perhaps that did not matter. He worked as a farmhand until he retired. Andriy said that his grandfather was now living with his parents in England, and that he always insisted on speaking Ukrainian with the family. There was a strong Ukrainian community in the area, made up of immigrants who left behind a life of poverty and hoped to make it in the UK. Most of them wanted nothing to do with the communists and were proud to have fought with the partisans in the war."

We had reached Rothschild Avenue, just a few minutes' walk from my hotel. It was close to midnight. Bats were flying silently among the old, gnarled trees. One bar was still open, and we stopped there for a final drink.

"It's strange that Andriy's grandfather came from Mierzyn," I said.

"Yes, we even ended up going there during my visit. It's a lovely little spot, though the village is shabby, or at least it was at the time."

"My mother was born in that village."

"Yes, I know, that was why I wanted to speak with you today, but so many other things got in the way," she said, smiling.

She really had extraordinary eyes. I had never seen such a shade of blue. It was not the pale watery kind common in northern Europe but something more akin to cobalt, so improbably set against her dark complexion.

"I recently read an interview with you where you mentioned your mother's birthplace," she said.

"See, but I know very little about that village."

"I actually think Andriy's grandfather left Ukraine after the war because of something that happened there. Thinking back to my trip to Ukraine, it seems to me that Andriy was always trying to decipher that. But at the time, I was much more focused on visiting the place from which my grandmother fled, the place my mother imagined as her last refuge from turmoil and abandonment. I guess both of us were looking for something without knowing what it was. It turns out that you can't be of much help to me, either."

"I am just interested in the facts," I said. "As a historian, I try to keep a distance, to not get emotionally involved."

The bar was closing, so we paid and walked slowly toward my hotel. The weight of everything that had happened over the past couple of weeks, residual jetlag, and the copious amount of wine we had drunk, suddenly overcame me. I stopped and leaned against one of those old trees as the bats whirled around me like in a nightmare.

"I did get involved," she said. "We ended up spending the night in my hotel. But of course, nothing was resolved, not even the facts."

ZAKLOTS

A few weeks after returning to North America, I received an email from Tali. "We never quite finished that conversation," she wrote. She attached a text she had written, along with several photos of the kibbutz cemetery. "A couple of days after you left, I went to visit your father's grave, but there was no tombstone yet. It's nice that he is buried next to your mother. He was a good man and always nice to my mother, even though she went on and on about Galicia. It took me a while to find the cemetery, it's tucked away at the far corner of the kibbutz, and no one seemed to be able to direct me there. But it's a beautiful little spot. I'm sorry I missed the funeral. I'll go there again when they put up the stone. Could you let me know when that happens? I stayed there for a while. It seems to tell a history that no one remembers any longer, of a kind of love and passion for a place that no longer exists, by people who are no longer alive, although someone must remember them, because there were fresh flowers everywhere, including on your parents' graves. The whole place felt so detached from the country as it is now. I don't think the next generation should be buried there. It would not belong. In any case, the place is quite full. Even your parents, who must have loved the kibbutz, considering that they chose it for their last resting place, are right at the edge. I don't think there's room for more than one additional person without blocking the path."

I wondered about my father's wife, who had told me that she too wanted to be buried next to him.

"I really wanted to tell you a little more about my trip to Ukraine," Tali continued. "Last time we met it was all a bit rushed, and I think by the end of the evening I had drunk too much and then, well, you had to leave. But maybe you will find some meaning in this account. Strangely, I know no one else to whom I can tell this story. I have never discussed more than the most general outlines of that trip with anyone.

"The next morning, we went down for breakfast at the George Hotel and the waiter seemed rather annoyed that I was not alone. He also did not appreciate my order of a second glass of orange juice, and grimly informed me that I would have to pay extra. Luckily, the *mlyntsi*, those Ukrainian blinis, were delicious and the tea strong. I felt warm and languid, watching Andriy who was consulting several maps and guidebooks.

"'I would suggest another hotel,' he said, motioning toward the stern waiter at the corner of the vast, mostly empty dining hall, with its peeling blue and yellow wallpaper. 'Did you know that before this hotel was built at the beginning of the last century, the same spot was occupied by the Russia Hotel?' He snickered. 'The Russians have always thought that we belonged to them.'

"'I booked this hotel because it seemed so central and had such big rooms,' I said.

"'Your room is certainly spacious, but the bed could use some upgrading,' he said, trying not to smile.

"'Some very prominent people stayed here. Balzac, Liszt, Ravel, even Sartre, though I have no idea what he might have been doing here.'

"'Well, they're all dead,' said Andriy. 'There's a much nicer new boutique hotel on the other side of the square.'

"He didn't say anything about who would be paying, but I didn't really mind. I had saved money for a long time for this trip, and I was not about to start counting pennies now. In any case, I liked Andriy, and everything was so cheap.

"You must be wondering why I am writing you this, after all we hardly know each other, even though we are, so to speak, family. Our roots—that thing I never believed in but began pulling at me—go back to the same place. I had traveled to many countries by the time I went to Ukraine, but never to Galicia, never to that fabled hometown, perhaps precisely because I had heard so much about it since childhood from my mother and grandmother and all those other Galitzianers I had encountered over the years. What I heard was so contradictory and so strongly felt and, in some ways, so terrifying, that I could not bring myself to go there.

"But at the same time, perhaps like my crazy mother, I had some inkling that a journey there might bring about some resolution, that it would be a journey not only in space but in time, to a pivotal point that changed lives forever with one brutal blow, irreversibly separating those who experienced the horror, and those who were not there and could never reconcile themselves to having lost that world and all it meant to them. The place and its people, all gone, the language, the gestures, the smells and the sights, erased from existence. That world had vanished like a puff of smoke, leaving us without any reference points, with nothing to fall back on, suspended in midair, knowing that at any given moment gravity might suck us into that black hole of time and we'd be completely lost.

"There was also that business with Andriy. I was 38 at the time, had never married, and did not want to have any children, not after my childhood and what my mother and my grandmother had gone through. I was independent and quite happy in my own way, or at least I thought I was. I had some friends, traveled a lot, and had not a few lovers, men I liked and who liked me, without any commitment but also not simple one-night-stands. Men who let me explore myself a little more without the oppressive know-it-all of our country and the speed with which we all tag and identify each other even before we begin to know those we encounter. Men who would show me around and teach me about their cultures, whether it was in Taipei or Buenos Aires, Berlin or Paris, London or New York. I was quite attractive and probably seemed exotic to those men. I was available but at the same time always kept myself protected from anything deeper that might push me over the edge.

"But I never thought of going to that hometown and I never thought of leaving Israel. I know that you left many years ago and made your peace with that, that you have a life in North America and don't suffer, as you told me, from that unbearable Israeli malaise of taking Israel with you wherever you go, living your provincial little Israeli life in any nest you build for yourself wherever you end up in the world, trying to force that pathetic nostalgia down your children and grandchildren's throats until you become a relic of a place that exists only in your memory. I needed to go back to Israel because it was only there that I could feel that particular kind of familiar homelessness that enabled me to pack my bags and travel, to places that were foreign and different and relieved me of that very sense of homelessness that had been there from the beginning and that I could not live without.

"Andriy was a different matter altogether. 'Those Ukrainian murderers,' my grandmother would always say, 'were worse than the Germans, they killed everyone. I would never want to go back there. Even when I went with Hannaleh to visit, just before all the killing began, who could have known? They were still so nice and polite, they would bow to you and remove their hats and smile, they'd offer you eggs and bread and milk in the villages, even though they were dirt poor. Who could have known that one day they would simply get up in the morning and slaughter everyone in the most horrible ways?' This is what my grandmother said, and apart from that one trip before the war she never left Israel, even though she was never happy there.

"In a way she too was always homeless. She never loved my grandfather Adolf, who was much older than her and died from cancer before I was born. Her lovers were mostly older married men who just broke her heart over and over again. Eventually she gave up on the whole business. When I was ten, she put an end to it all by going somewhere along the Yarkon river and swallowing a massive dose of painkillers. A search party was organized and even I joined a group of neighbors and their children. By the time another group found her, she was dead.

"So for me to take a Ukrainian lover, although he was actually British, might have seemed completely unnatural, abnormal even. But it did not feel that way, and what I felt for Andriy was different, both because he was a gentle and sweet man, but also because he felt part of something I was looking for and could never find. Something familiar in its strangeness and warm and loving that I had not felt before. I even began to worry during those two weeks that I might be falling in love, because just like me, he had been drawn to a place that he knew only from the stories of others and shared the feeling that some past horror had come to shape his life decades later.

39

"We moved to that boutique hotel, and he was right, it felt very different and it was there that we drew much closer. I remember lying in bed with him that afternoon, hearing the traffic from the square through the half open window, the breeze carrying the first whiffs of spring. The room was remarkably modern and clean. Stroking Andriy's almost hairless chest I only wanted to enjoy this bliss for as long as possible.

"Then he said, 'Do you want to go to Porushennya?'

"It took me a moment to understand, because this was not the name I had always heard at home. 'Zaklots,' they always called it in Yiddish, or Zakłócenie, the proper Polish name of our hometown. Now it was known by its Ukrainian name, which of course made sense, because now only Ukrainians lived there. Still, for me it was Zaklots. 'Yes,' I said to Andriy, 'let's go there tomorrow.'"

TOVA

Tali's account ended abruptly at this point. "I'll send you more installments soon," she promised. Over the next few days, I was too busy to think about what she had written, but during the weekend I spent some time looking through my family records and discovered an old letter my mother had written to me a couple of years before her death for a research project I was planning at the time. There was something uncanny about seeing her neat, rather stylized Hebrew script all those years later. I could hear her voice, her slight Polish accent and faultless, deliberate diction. She never took much to typing and while I normally do not like reading handwritten documents, even though in my profession I often have to, holding that long letter written in her own hand felt infinitely closer to her than any typescript could have done. I do not think of myself as sentimental and accepted my mother's death from cancer as part of the cycle of life. But I would have liked her to live a little longer to enjoy her retirement and to get to know my younger children. This posthumous encounter put me in a melancholy mood, and I decided to dedicate Sunday to reading, transcribing, and translating the letter into English.

"Your grandfather Yakov and his younger brother Adolf were born, as far as I know, in a little village called Mierzyn, where I too was born," she wrote. "I still remember it as very beautiful, right on the banks of a big river, the Dniester, I think, or was it the Dnieper? I used to play there as a girl. I remember we would go to the forest to pick mushrooms and berries. We'd often sit on the bank of that huge river. You don't see things like that in Israel, which has only the Yarkon and the Jordan. This was a river so wide that you could hardly see the other bank. Logs would be floating downriver, tied to each other like vast rafts, all the way down to the Black Sea.

"My grandfather was an estate manager for the Grafina, the countess who owned the estate together with her sister. She was a widow, and her sister never married. Their family had lived there for generations. I think they were close to our family, because my grandfather's father had also been the estate manager. My grandfather lived in a house next to the farm buildings, while the Grafina and her sister lived in a beautiful old mansion, surrounded by tall trees. There was also a little chapel there, I remember, because the Polish nobility were Roman Catholic. The peasants on the farm were all Greek Catholic Ukrainians and had their own church in the village. I don't think there was a synagogue because our family were the only Jews, so on the holidays they would go to the synagogue in a nearby town. But I know they lived a Jewish life in the village; they were very traditional, my grandparents.

"The boys, Yakov and Adolf, were big fellows, tall and strong. They worked on the farm and were out all day and didn't have much time for school. Father told me that as teenagers they used to play with the Grafina's two sons, who were about the same age. They especially liked soccer and would organize teams from the village boys and have real matches. The whole village would turn out to watch. It would be one team of Poles and Jews and some of the estate stableboys, and one team of Ukrainian peasants, and there were drinks and treats for everyone. People knew their place and their faith and there was not much social mixing, except among the children, but they also had respect for each other and a sense of dignity. In any case, that's what my father used to say. Was there resentment, or jealousy, or hatred? I don't know. We know what happened later. But Father never talked about that, and I don't remember any. I was a very young girl when we lived in the village."

My mother came to Palestine with her parents and two brothers a few years before the war. But she spent the first decade of her life first in Mierzyn and then in Zaklots, which she often called by its Polish name Zakłócenie, perhaps because she went to a Polish public school there, and had vivid memories of those years. She also used to speak with her mother a great deal about the old country, but not with me, probably because she thought I would have no interest in those stories. My grandfather, even though normally he was not much of a talker, loved to tell us grandchildren all sorts of fables and folktales he must have remembered from his own childhood, growing up surrounded by Ukrainian peasants. I don't think he told my mother, who was his favorite, any of those tales when she was a child. I suppose you can't be nostalgic about a place if you are still living there. After they moved to Palestine, he worked such long hours that he would fall asleep as soon as he had his dinner and leave home the following day before dawn. So it was only us grandchildren who heard these tales in the brief period between his retirement and his death.

"Rochaleh," my mother wrote, "was the youngest child and my grandfather's favorite, and I remember that everyone used to call her the jewel in the crown. Even though she too grew up on the farm, she had ambitions and wanted to get a proper education. When I think about that now, she seems to have been a little like me. You know your uncles were big, hardworking men, but cared little for school, whereas I always wanted to study and learn more about everything: literature, poetry, history, psychology. I only have childhood memories of Rochaleh, but I remember my father always speaking about her as the educated and striving one, as he later spoke about me. Only she never really had an opportunity to realize any of her dreams, because of the way people lived in those days and the restrictions on Jews and women.

"Then she was murdered, although how that happened, nobody knows. She and her husband, who did have a university degree, and their daughter, who was about the same age as poor Hannaleh. You know Hannaleh, she was never quite right in the head. They did not surface after the war, so they must have been murdered by the Germans.

"I too could have made more of myself, had it not been for your father and the children, but how can you compare? In any case, your grandfather and his brother were both physically robust men, but very different. Grandfather, as you know, was always religious and respectful toward his father, who was rather an authoritarian figure that everyone feared a bit. Even I kept my distance from him. It was expected that Grandfather would continue the family tradition and succeed his father as estate manager. But Grandfather was a kind, soft-spoken man, very unlike his father, and to run an estate with all those rough-and-ready farmhands and peasants, one needed to be not just big and strong but also a bit of a bully.

"So not long after I was born the family moved to Zakłócenie. We lived in a big house on Railroad Street, divided into two parts, one for my grandfather and one for the rest of the family. My grandfather still spent most of his time on the estate until he retired, but by then we had already left Poland. I think my father helped with the business as long as we lived in Zakłócenie and did all kinds of buying and selling. He became increasingly engaged with the Zionists and began talking about going to Palestine. But it took several years before we actually went, by which time it was almost too late.

"Adolf," she wrote, "was completely different. He was volatile and headstrong and never wanted any involvement in the family business. Once they moved to Zakłócenie, he got in with the communists, who were actually all Jews in the town. From that point on he could hardly ever sleep at home because the Polish police was always after him. My grandfather wanted nothing to do with him, because Adolf had become what he called a complete goy with no respect for religion and tradition. He fancied himself a revolutionary, although he was in fact rather a fragile man and quickly disintegrated when confronted with adversity. That was what happened to him when he went to Palestine, a couple of years before us.

"The story of how he went to Palestine is interesting. He was no Zionist, but things apparently got too hot for him in Galicia, and he had to get away. For a Jew it was very hard to leave at that time, there was the Great Depression and unemployment and no country wanted to let in immigrants, especially Jews. So, unless he wanted to cross over into the Soviet Union, which he was not foolish enough to consider, given all the news that was seeping in about mass hunger in Ukraine, it looked like the only viable option was to obtain a certificate of immigration to Palestine. For this purpose he joined one of the Zionist organizations in the city, and, being young and strong and unburdened by a wife and children, in other words constituting the right human material for building the Jewish state, he was promised to get a certificate in no time at all. But then things dragged on for weeks and months.

"While he was waiting impatiently for his certificate, Adolf got to know Tova, Hannaleh's mother. Adolf was in his later twenties, and

Tova was barely 18. She was desperate to get out of Zakłócenie, and he was kindhearted and increasingly excited about the prospect of finally leaving a place where the police were chasing after him, the Jews despised him, the Poles and Ukrainians saw him as an agent of Jewish communism, and his own family was at their wits' end as to what to do with him. Tova suggested that they register as married with the municipal registrar, without involving any religious authorities, so that she could travel with him to Palestine as a wife. Adolf saw no reason to turn her down; she was pretty as a picture and a bit of a flirt. It also did not seem like such a serious proposition, as the idea was that they would annul the marriage and go their separate ways once they arrived in Palestine.

"Under the law, they first had to prove that they belonged to no acknowledged religious organization in order to register for a civil marriage. As a communist, Adolf was in the clear and the authorities were glad to be rid of him. Tova, whose father had been killed fighting for the emperor in World War I, and whose mother had died in the cholera epidemic during the Russian occupation, was raised in a Jewish orphanage. The wealthy ladies supporting that institution were only too pleased to provide the documentation that would enable their ward to begin a new life in the Promised Land with a man who vowed to disown communism and become a good Zionist and provider. Once the marriage was registered and the certificate issued, they hurriedly packed their few belongings and boarded the train for the long journey to the Romanian port of Constanza. From there Adolf posted a letter to his parents, informing them of his secret marriage and his plans for a new revolutionary life in Eretz Israel, fighting for Jewish and Arab worker solidarity against the oppression of Zionist capitalism and British colonialism.

"Only things did not turn out as expected. On the ship, Adolf fell in love with Tova, the kind of love that only a revolutionary is capable of, full of sound and fury and entirely divorced from the object of his love. He was a handsome man and must have made an impression on this young woman who had spent her entire life waiting to be rescued from an orphanage. It must have all been very romantic. But life in Palestine quickly eroded all those tender feelings. I should know, because I remember how it was when we arrived here, how hard life was and how, although I was only 11, I quickly realized that I had left my childhood behind in Zakłócenie and would never get it back. I was very lonely because my parents were never at home. They would go to work early in the morning and come back after sundown. Back in Zakłócenie, my mother had not worked. My father would not have allowed it even if she had wanted to. She would always be there when I came back from school, and we also had a *shikse*, a Ukrainian maid, who was young and fun for me to have around. I had friends in school and in the neighborhood, and every summer we would go on a long trip in a horse-drawn cart to my mother's family in a little village called Vozhnor, which was Ukrainian with only a few Jewish families living around the market square.

"Vozhnor was close to the Czeremosz River, and on the other side was Bukovina, which was then in Romania. We'd often go to the riverbank and play with the local kids and eat *mamaliga* with fish. At night the family would lock all the doors and close the heavy wooden shutters even if it was hot and airless in the house. They said that some antisemitic villagers had already broken into other Jewish homes.

"Vozhnor was where my uncles lived, Szymen, who went with his bride to South America before the war, and Chaim the violinist. I still remember him playing at family functions. There was also another brother, Ovadia. My father told me that Chaim and Ovadia were at one point in hiding with their families in the town of Vosok, which was nearby, but were denounced and murdered. That's all I know. Their father had died when they were very small, so all four children, my mother and her brothers, were raised by their mother and grandfather, who lived a very long life and died just before the war. I still remember him sitting outside the house, his beard reaching down to his chest, warming his bones in the summer sun. Occasionally he would wave his hand in front of his face and mutter to himself, 'enough with that,' as if he were trying to chase away some nagging old sorrow.

"Tova did not have such fond memories of our hometown and I remember her telling me once how hard it was to grow up as an orphan in Zakłócenie, where so much of people's lives revolved around their extended families. Even some of the children in the orphanage had aunts and uncles and other relatives who would take them to their homes for the Sabbath or bring them extra food, fresh fruits, or a piece of cake, and might even pay a tutor to help them with their studies. She had no one because her parents had died soon after arriving in the area, and other family members were hard to find during World War I when the Russians occupied the town and many Jews fled to Vienna and Prague. Families were torn apart and some were never reunited. Many died from epidemics and hunger, as well as in pogroms by Cossacks.

"It was no surprise that Tova so urgently wanted to leave, even if it meant marrying a man she did not know who was a decade older

48

than her and considered a bad apple. That's why I could never understand how Hannaleh developed such a yearning to go back to our town, which her mother had so wanted to leave. I think Tova could never really be happy, because of her wretched childhood and her nature. I remember being dazzled by her when we came to Palestine. She was such a beautiful young woman, and I was still a very impressionable girl. I had never seen anyone so glamorous, certainly not in dusty, provincial Tel Aviv where we initially lived, sharing Adolf and Tova's two-room house. She always had such lovely clothes and beautiful jewelry. I remember how she would carefully touch up her lipstick in a little mirror. She wore perfume every day. She simply did not belong in our environment. Poor uncle Adolf worked very hard to pay for her finery. He had a job in construction and had no time left over for communism. Instead, he became obsessed with making his wife happy, which she never was. Very few people knew that Tova had a baby, a girl who was born not long after we arrived. I don't remember ever seeing her pregnant, and she did all she could to ignore that baby's existence, maybe because she had never really had the chance to be a young woman before suddenly becoming a wife and a mother in exile.

"And so, Tova was unhappy in Palestine and may have regretted leaving Zakłócenie and certainly marrying poor Adolf. Still, it was quite a surprise to everyone when she announced that she wanted to go back for a visit in 1939. Adolf had to scramble and work extra hours to come up with the boat fare. I don't know if she already had lovers then, but I remember that there were rumors, because why would a married woman and the mother of a small child dress up and behave so coquettishly instead of finding a job and caring for her baby? In retrospect I think she felt very lonely and isolated, as so many people who came over at the time did. She had no family to fall back on, so the world was closing in on her before she had ever had a chance to make anything out of herself. Perhaps the visit to Europe was a way of retracing her steps.

"But it was too late. The clouds of war were gathering over Europe and all paths would be sealed within months of her trip. She also told me that she wanted to visit my aunt Rochaleh, the jewel in the crown. They had become friends just before she and Adolf went to Palestine. Rochaleh was just five years older and had her own ambitions for a different life. Those too were disappointed. She lived in the house with us in Zakłócenie before she married her university graduate, Max Reichert. It's a wonder that I can still remember his name. Maybe it was thanks to that marriage that she came to be called the jewel in the crown, because in those days, in our family of villagers and estate managers and millers and petty merchants, who would have ever dreamed of a university education or marrying someone with one?

"That marriage also did not end up the way either of them had expected, although they were not unhappy, I think. Max had hoped to find a teaching position, if not at the university, then at least at a gymnasium, or even a good elementary school. But in the whole of Galicia, it was almost impossible for a young Jewish academic to find a teaching position at this time, because the Polish government thought there were too many Jews in educational institutions, and they should be grateful for being allowed to even study. They should not take jobs from Polish university graduates.

"Max could not teach, and Rochaleh could not be the wife of a professor. My grandfather proposed to Max that he could run his business in one of the nearby villages, where he had a mill and a store. This was a good business, that urgently needed a new manager because old Cohen, who had run it for many years, had fallen ill and Cohen's son, God protect us from such sorrow, had become a Zionist and gone to Palestine, leaving his old parents and unwed sister to fend for themselves. It was a compromise for Max and Rochaleh, but she was pregnant, and they had to make a living.

"Living in my grandfather's home was cramped and oppressive, even though it was a large building set a little back from the main road leading to the train station. Max was said to have been a brilliant student, and could apparently lecture on many topics, such as literature and history, poetry and art, quite eloquently. When it came to business, he was not such a great find, as Rochaleh soon discovered. He did not know how to interact with the local villagers, was easily cheated, and preferred to sit in the corner of the little store engrossed in a book. It was Rochaleh who had to care for the baby and run the business, selling thread, buttons, leather products, goose fat, and cooking oil to the locals. It turned out that she had inherited her father's skills. Her husband, even though he had left the fold and was hardly ever seen in the synagogue except during the High Holidays, behaved just like a yeshiva lad and studied all day, neither helping with the business nor much with the baby.

"What became of Max and Rochaleh in the last years before the war I know from Tova. I distinctly recall her telling me that she and Rochaleh had so much in common, though Tova was 24 and Rochaleh almost 30. Both of them had little girls, Hannaleh was four and Rochaleh's Judit was just a year older, and both were married to men who did not quite accomplish what they had set out to do and were made unhappy not only by their own failures but also by their wives' disappointment in them. So here were these two women asking themselves where they had gone wrong and if they could still repair the damage, one by leaving and the other by returning.

"The highlight of Tova's visit was the trip they all made together to the family's old village of Mierzyn on the banks of the Dniester, or was it the Dnieper? Tova said they were so happy and carefree there, just like little children with all of their lives still ahead of them, running through the forest, watching the logs float down the river, playing with the girls on the beach. They would sit by the fireplace late into the night and dream about their futures as if nothing stood between them and their desires but the darkness of the night that would soon lift with a glorious sunrise over the vast expanse of trees and water. They wandered through the old house, where the new estate manager, a young energetic man keen to modernize the estate, hosted them. He found the old Grafina to be too set in her ways, especially since the passing of her sister, but got on well with the two sons. Unfortunately, they were mostly away in Lviv and Warsaw and had little interest in farming.

"This Dmytro and his wife Oksana had been great hosts and served them delicious dairy kasza. Our region was famous for its groats, from which *kasza* is made. Oksana was expecting and already a little heavy. She was a young woman with delicate features and a beautiful, thick, blond braid. Tova and the rest of the family were not very interested in Dmytro's agricultural plans, least of all Max, who had reluctantly agreed to come with them but kept seeking opportunities to withdraw somewhere and stick his nose into his book. But they listened because they did not want to offend Dmytro, possibly the first Ukrainian to ever manage that old Polish estate. He was so proud to have bought off the Szumers, whose name had been linked to this estate for as long as anyone in the village could remember.

"Dmytro was actually a Hutsul, one of those people who lived mostly in the mountains, and he told them that up there, in the Carpathians, there were very different Jews. Muscle Jews, he called them, who worked as loggers and carpenters and blacksmiths and were just like their neighbors, only that they prayed to the Jewish God. Where he came from, he said, everyone was as poor as the next person, but all were free and independent. 'Things there in the mountains are not as they are here,' he said, where people in the village speak badly of the Jews behind their backs and are only waiting for an opportunity to beat them. The villagers, he said, told him they were glad that the Szumers had finally left them in peace and that one of their own was in charge. All they needed now was to finally be rid of the old Grafina and her arrogant sons and all would be well. 'We Hutsuls are not like that,' Dmytro said, 'we don't care who your mother was and who you pray to as long as you work hard and are honest, and that has paid off in my case. My father and my brothers have a good logging business in the mountains. We saved every penny and now I have set myself up here in the plains. Soon my old parents will join us and live in comfort for the rest of their lives with us and their grandchildren.'

"Tova told me that above the fireplace, close to the table where we had celebrated many Shabbat dinners and Passover seders, Dmytro had hung one of the only items he had brought with him from the mountains, a large axe with a broad, hand-forged blade. It had a beautifully carved long wooden handle and had been in his family for generations. It was a symbol of the tough and proud Hutsul mountain-dwelling nation, where every man must own a *bartka*, as he called it, a tool that serves every purpose. It could be a walking stick and a hammer or be used for cutting down trees or fending off wild beasts and robbers. He took the *bartka* off the wall and let the guests touch it. Max feigned interest and gave a short lecture, during which he became increasingly animated, on the ancient history of axes, possibly the first tool invented by man for work and war. He went on to enumerate various other types of axes, such as the famous American Indian tomahawk, which could be thrown with great accuracy and lethality in battle. 'Well,' Dmytro had said, 'I don't know about Indians, but it's an ancient Hutsul tool.'

"Rochaleh later told Tova that Max, who was fluent in German, had a collection of Karl May's books on the adventures of the Wild West hero Old Shatterhand and his inseparable Apache friend Winnetou. You remember those books that you loved so much," my mother wrote, "which I used to bring you from the library, and you would pretend to be sick and stay in bed reading them instead of going to school? Rochaleh had giggled and said that maybe that was where Max had learned about those Indian axes.

"In the afternoon one of the stableboys, Mykhailo, a nice but taciturn lad, wearing clothes so tattered that they seemed to be made from discarded rags, and walking barefoot, took them across the meadow toward the Grafina's house. They met her two sons, Władek and Janek, who were there with their families over the summer. They were tall, elegantly dressed middle-aged men, very different from Tova and Rochaleh's husbands, the doting old revolutionary and the downcast scholar. They reminisced about the days when they were boys on the estate, playing soccer on the village green with the two Schumer boys. Leaning on their walking canes and smoking long pipes, Władek and Janek asked how Yakov and Adolf were doing in Palestine. 'They did well to leave,' they said. 'This place is going to the dogs.' Behind them, the mansion was visibly falling apart, with its plaster peeling and some of the windowpanes missing. The garden was covered with weeds and the general impression was that of a charming Italian ruin you see in travel books, not a dwelling for aristocrats.

"There were butterflies everywhere, of all colors and shapes, flying up and down in unison like a vast multicolored blanket as the little girls chased them across the meadow. They had quickly become firm friends and were utterly happy together. Hannaleh was heartbroken when they eventually had to board the train for the long journey back, passing through endless fields heavy with grain and vast forests stretching as far as the eye could see. From the train window they waved to village girls leading cows to pasture. The geese were running alongside the railroad tracks and Hannaleh cried and cried as if they would never see them again. They never did.

"So, this was Tova's visit, and a few weeks after she returned, everything fell apart. First came the war, and everyone over there was sucked into that black hole and never heard of again. No one ever came out to tell us what happened, except for my father's cousin Yitzhak, or Izi, as they used to call him. He showed up shortly after the end of the war, but my father would have nothing to do with him. I never could understand why. He was, after all, the only survivor, one of those few burning sticks snatched from the fire, as we referred to them at the time.

"But there was a rumor that Izi had been a Kapo, or a policeman, and on those few occasions when he came to visit, a handsome man, like all the Szumers, my father, who was a kind and gentle soul, was polite to him but remained cold and distant. After a while he stopped coming. People said that he had gone to Canada, but others insisted that he took his own life. Who knows? He might have been able to tell us what happened, but as far as I know he never did. Maybe he felt guilty, or no one would listen.

"After the war, Tova became increasingly lonely, overwhelmed by the feeling that she could never have a life with Adolf and that she could never be a mother to Hannaleh. The girl was just left on the wayside without anyone caring for her. I tried to take care of her a little, but she was a difficult child. She never quite matured, and was such a sad little thing. No child should be abandoned like that. Her mother went from bad to worse. She had endless, meaningless affairs, ever more desperate as she grew older. She did not take good care of herself and toward the end looked shabby and worn out.

"Then there was Adolf's horrible illness, a mouth cancer that led to several operations, literally cutting off parts of his face, which had been quite handsome once, like your grandfather's. You didn't want to see him when we went to visit because you were scared of the way he looked. After he died, Tova abruptly stopped seeing men, and tried to get closer to Hannaleh, although that never quite worked out. She spent more and more time locked up in her little apartment with the blinds drawn. By then we were no longer very close, in part because I was very busy. Then, as you know, she killed herself. She had just turned 60 and left nothing behind, although I heard somewhere that there is a granddaughter."

I had only read that letter once before, when I received it, and not very closely, perhaps because my mother was still alive, and I thought that I could just speak to her about its contents. Maybe I did not quite understand why she chose to relate this entire story in the first place. At the time I was still only vaguely aware of her own difficulties with my father and did not want to know too much about them, as is the case, I think, with many children.

"I don't know why I wrote you all this," she concluded her letter, "but I thought you might want to know, especially now that you have become interested in our town, for which I am very grateful. No one knows what happened to our family. I sometimes have nightmares about Rochaleh and little Judit and see the most horrible visions of how they must have been murdered. But maybe I have been reading too many stories from that time. In any case, I thought you should know."

For some reason, knowing that she herself had died only a few years after writing this letter, made me read it very differently, as if it were not just about Tova and Rochaleh and Uncle Adolf but also about my mother, about her own loneliness and longing for the world of her childhood. There was a sense of her never quite being at home in her new homeland and in the family she raised. But that might be my own projection. I do remember writing to her at the time that she should publish this letter, or some version of it, that it was like a sketch for a novel. But she dismissed this idea with a laugh when we spoke on the phone, and when we next met in person she was already ill and nothing came of it.

ANDRIY

Several weeks passed before Tali emailed me again, by which time I thought that her eagerness to share her story with me had waned. Maybe she had gone on another trip, I thought. Her email merely stated, "Here is more," and attached to it was a long document. I was very busy with teaching, completing an article, writing letters of reference, and other professional and personal issues, so it took me a few days to carve out the time to sit down and read it. I was also a little unsure as to why I had become mixed up in this tangled web of stories, a good 20 years after my mother's passing. It was as if my father's death had triggered something that I could not access all those years ago. Perhaps he had been the obstacle.

"I am sorry it took me so long," Tali wrote. "After sending you the last message I was suddenly filled with doubts. Why was I telling you all these stories about myself? Are you interested at all or just being nice to me, as your father was to my mother? Do you think I am crazy? You said you like facts and prefer to keep a distance, but for me the facts are confused with memories and figments of my imagination, and I can never maintain the proper distance, if there is ever such a thing in personal histories, relationships, and inherited family memories.

"I was also confused because of that night we spent in Tel Aviv and what it meant to you, and to me. In talking to you about Andriy I somehow confused the two of you and had to sort things out. Well, enough with the excuses, I just want to explain that I agreed to go to Wellington, New Zealand, where my agency now has a branch. They have some management issues related to increased tourism from Israel, and they need an old hand like me to help them out a bit. I don't know if you've ever been here, but it's a lovely town, if you don't mind terrifying landings in high winds into a narrow bay tucked between jagged mountains. I think you would enjoy walking up the steep streets of this town. The move took a fair amount of time.

"But after getting settled, I decided to take a few days off in Queenstown, on Lake Wakatipu in South Island, an absolutely divine spot. I go for hikes during the day and have been trying to write the rest of this account in the evenings. It's about as far away as one can go, so I guess I am distancing myself, as you suggested. But the rest of what I have to say involves being much closer, to the extent that I sometimes lose focus, as when you walk right up to a painting and see nothing but meaningless brushstrokes. I have been thinking about what happened between me and Andriy. I hadn't thought about it for a long time and telling you about that meeting brought it all back. It was obviously not natural for either of us, yet at the same time it felt as if we had both waited for that moment for much of our lives. I don't mean this in the sense of some romantic story, love at first sight and all that, which it was not, but more as an encounter that opened us to ourselves.

"I was raised to think about Ukrainians as murderers. Of course, none of us knows what happened in our town or to our families in any detail, but we know the general outlines. People around me, and probably around you too, always said that the Ukrainians were worse than the Germans; that they slaughtered and tortured people, including their own neighbors, people they had lived next door to for generations. They had not changed since the days of Khmelnytsky. They slaughtered Jews in the Cossack uprising, they slaughtered them during the Russian Revolution, and they slaughtered them in the Holocaust. 'It's in their blood,' people said. 'They drank Jew-hatred with their mother's milk.' You know all that.

"There I was, feeling so warm and safe and utterly open with this lovely man, who seemed as comfortable as a fish in water walking around Lviv with me, chatting with the locals, showing me the best sites in this beautiful, though still quite run-down, city. Strolling with him down one of the streets leading to the vast Lychakiv cemetery, a tram came hurtling down the hill at breakneck speed. In the front a rather buxom young woman with a smart uniform sat at the controls and was repeatedly crossing herself. I asked Andriy, 'Is she afraid of crashing? This doesn't look too safe to me.'

"He laughed and said, 'No, the tram passes by several churches, that's why she is crossing herself,' as if 40 years of communism had not made a dint in people's attitudes. 'This place was called the Łyczaków cemetery in Polish times,' he said as we passed through the gates, 'and it's filled with graves of famous Poles and Ukrainians, lying side by side. The cemetery has always been a site of pilgrimage for young couples and families on the weekends. But people also come simply because it's so beautiful.'

"As I found out, there are many memorials there, to Poles who fought the Ukrainians and to Ukrainians who fought the Poles, a bewildering mess of statues and tombstones so densely packed together that you can't quite tell where one ends and the other begins. We Jews are totally excluded from the story, even though we ended up paying the highest price. But you know all that, I think I even read something you wrote a few years ago on memory and erasure in this region. By the time we walked into the cemetery, what had started as a cloudy morning had turned into a gloriously sunny, though chilly, day. Andriy was hugging me to keep me warm, and afterward we went to a nearby restaurant and had soup and brandy. I asked him how he felt about this cemetery and if anyone in his family ever spoke about that period.

"'My grandfather Mykhailo,' Andriy said, warming his brandy in his hands and looking more pensive than I had seen him before, 'only spent a few years in school, although he can read and write Ukrainian and English. He, in fact, took a liking to reading history and fiction, especially after he retired, but he spent most of his life as a farmer. Only recently did he move in with my parents, which has not been simple as he and my father have always had a rather tense relationship. He is not a big talker, my grandfather, but after he's had a few drinks, he begins to reminisce about the war, which my father has always detested. He would regularly say that my father could not imagine what it was like and compare it to the cushy life we live in the UK, where there's always food on the table, you can get a good education, and you don't have to fear for your life.

"'My father was born after the war and didn't want anything to do with all this ancient Ukrainian stuff. My grandfather was always going to meetings of veterans, singing patriotic songs, and getting drunk on vodka and memories of the lost homeland they could never return to. Father wanted to be a proper Brit and did become one, even though he married a Ukrainian girl, which is a bit funny. My mother is actually half Russian and half Jewish but from Ukraine, which makes me a quarter Jewish, although growing up I didn't quite understand that. I just took for granted various things my mother did, such as lighting memorial candles for her grandparents who were murdered in Babi Yar.

"'I was and still am close to my grandfather. I used to love sitting with him in his little kitchen. My grandmother would make borsht and potatoes, and I'd gobble up her food and his stories of how little farm boys like himself, peasants who had always been treated like dirt by the arrogant Polish lords and their Jewish lackeys, finally took up arms and rose up against them to fight for independence and equality. They wanted to kick out the whole lot of them, foreigners and invaders, Polacks and Kikes, and also the Krauts and the Muscovites. They never stood a chance and they knew it, but they fought like devils and gained the dignity and self-respect they and all their forefathers since Bohdan Khmelnytsky had always been denied.

"'Even if they eventually lost and the damn communists won and took over their land, at least they knew they had fought a good fight and could hope that one day the entire rotten Russian state would collapse and Ukraine would finally be for the Ukrainians. When Gorbachev started dismantling the Soviet Union, and the whole thing came apart like a house of cards, my grandfather became obsessed with the news. He was just overwhelmed when Ukraine became independent in 1991. I was sure that he would go there at least to visit, now that the communists were gone, but he never did. He said he was too old and sick, although he seemed perfectly healthy to me. He was only in his late sixties then.'

"I was a bit taken aback by this story," Tali wrote, "because I didn't know what Andriy meant when he said that his grandfather had fought for Ukrainian independence. Was he in the resistance? I had always thought that the resistance was against the Germans, and that the Red Army liberated all those people in Eastern Europe from German occupation, although I did know that they later installed communist dictatorships there. And what was all that about the Jews? The Ukrainians were fighting to liberate themselves from us? I thought they had collaborated with the Germans and persecuted us. I had come to Ukraine to try to understand what it was about this place that my mother could not free herself from, and here I was listening to this man who had become my transient lover talk about liberation from Jewish rule? Did he know who he was speaking to? So I asked Andriy what his grandfather had done during the war.

"He put his hand on mine.

"'When I became a bit older,' he said, 'I began reading about all this, because it was pretty hard to make sense of my grandfather's stories. My father never spoke about any of this, and would always just say, "Olga, should we let the boy be exposed to my old man's nationalist dribble?" My mother, who had imbibed a good deal of communist education in her youth, would say in her typical manner, "Grandfather is a dear old man but also a bloody fascist and antisemite and Andriy should stay away from him." But they didn't have the heart to stop me and, in any case, they were always too busy to know where I was going. I am the only one in my family who is trying to learn more about that period, which is not easy, because to this day people have such polar opinions about it even here in Ukraine. That's why I decided to spend some time here after I defended my thesis.'

63

"I had never asked him what he did before coming to work at a tourist agency in Lviv," Tali wrote. "It turned out he had studied history at St. Antony's College, Oxford, finishing his doctorate the previous year. This made him the first in his family with an advanced degree, and only the second, after his mother, to have attended university.

"I prodded him again about his grandfather's experience during the war.

"'Well, obviously I still don't know all the details, getting a straight story from him is very difficult. He's become a bit more morose and withdrawn with age and living with my parents has not been easy for anyone. My mother can be quite curt with him, and my father tends to ignore him. He spends most of the day watching television while they go out to work, my father to the auto shop and my mum to the school where she is now headmistress. Sometimes he reads old Ukrainian novels. His favorite author is Ivan Franko. You've probably never heard of him.

"'In terms of the war, my impression is that toward the end of the occupation, Grandfather joined the Ukrainian insurgents when they turned against the Germans, and then, after the Red Army kicked out the Wehrmacht, fought the Russians too, because they wanted to establish a free Ukraine. I know now that many of these insurgents first served as policemen under the Germans and helped them murder Jews, but my grandfather never mentioned this, and I believe he had nothing to do with these crimes because he was just a farm boy in Myryn. We can go there the day after tomorrow. There were no Jews there at the time.

"'I think that when he heard about the insurgents, like so many other peasant boys, my grandfather thought that he could finally extricate himself from the muck and destitution and humiliation of life on the farm and do something important. With a gun and a uniform would come dignity and respect. Maybe he also wanted to take his revenge on his oppressors. This was a horrible time, the insurgents were slaughtering Polish communities and murdering any surviving Jews they encountered. Did my grandfather take part in any of this? I don't know, he has always evaded my questions.

"'He prefers to go on and on about how bitterly they fought against armed Polish bands and Soviet partisans, and how after the Bolsheviks came back the NKVD hunted them down. They would deport entire villages as punishment for harboring insurgents, killing his comrades one by one, until he was the only one left to tell the tale. After he finally escaped to the West, he spent many months in refugee camps and then in a displaced persons camp, before eventually making his way to Britain. There he was sent to work in Gloucestershire, and his life reverted to what it had been before; the same daily drudgery of farm work peppered with occasional nationalist celebrations with other veterans, without any prospects of moving up the social ladder. His son benefited from the British school system and managed to make a better life for himself, though.

"'For Grandfather, I am sure, those months as an insurgent were the best time of his life and their memory has sustained his sense of self-worth to this day. Still, I cannot understand how he reconciles that with the kinds of crimes he must have seen or been complicit in, the killings of so many innocent civilians. Is it possible that he was spared all this? Did he repress those memories? Is he secretly proud of his actions? The more I learned about what happened there, and the more I read about the Holocaust, the less I too could reconcile my childhood image of Grandfather with what I now imagined he did during the war. But we may never know. In any case, this is the reason why I wanted to go to his village. I have planned to do so ever since I came to Lviv, but have delayed and delayed. Now that you are here, we can go together, you to see your ancestral town, and me to see my ancestral village. Like you, I'm not quite sure what we'll find there, so perhaps it's better not to go alone.'

"You can imagine that this was not an easy conversation for me," Tali wrote. "When he first told me about his grandfather, I had formed an image in my mind of a poor peasant who had somehow survived the turmoil of the war and managed to start a new life in England. Now I was hearing the story of a man who fought on the side of the nationalists, probably collaborated with the Nazis in the mass murder of Jews, saw the Red Army not as liberators but oppressors, and eventually fled to Britain to avoid being strung up or sent to the Gulag by the Soviets. And this gentle Andriy, sitting with me in the café, nursing his second brandy and stroking my hand, probably known at Oxford as the bright and handsome Andy, had spent his childhood being brainwashed by that hateful old man.

"Why did Andriy go back to Ukraine? What was he hoping to find in that village? Then again, I thought, what am I looking for in Zaklots? I knew about my own unhappiness, my sense of rootlessness, my need to always be on the road and my fear of being sucked into some black hole of listlessness and depression; my terror of reenacting my mother's and grandmother's fate. But Andriy seemed so perfectly happy and accomplished, comfortable in his own skin and ready to launch a successful academic career after a brief sojourn in his ancestral land. What was he looking for? I looked into his eyes, which now appeared more gray than green, thinking that I didn't know anything about him, not really.

"'I was afraid of going there on my own,' he said. 'I'm not like you. You look so strong and resolute; you must have acquired those traits from growing up in Israel. There were a couple of Israeli students at St. Antony's with me. They were like you, charismatic, not taking any nonsense, straightforward, outspoken, but also funny and friendly. They were the first Israelis I met in my life, and I thought to myself that they were not at all like the characters my grandfather spoke about; those greedy, shifty, exploitative, money-grubbing Jews of his stories. He couldn't have known too many Jews in his tiny little village, anyway. You lot must be the successful product of the Zionist revolution,' he snickered.

"My hand was growing fidgety under his and Andriy continued speaking. 'I'm not like that. I am the grandson of a peasant and the son of a mechanic in a class-ridden society where those even an inch above you look down on you from their own private Olympus. I don't know how well you know Britain. Moving up the social ladder leaves you scarred for life and having a mother who is a foreigner and speaks with a funny accent doesn't help. My father grew up on a farm with two Ukrainian-speaking parents. My grandmother also came from Ukraine, courtesy of the Germans who brought her to the Reich as forced labor; so they met in Germany. But they wanted their child to move up in life, and sent him to a vocational school, where he trained to be a mechanic. He is very good with his hands but has no intellectual interests. He works all day, goes to the pub with his mates, comes home for supper, and goes to sleep.

"'It's funny, but my grandfather is the one who became interested in books, maybe I inherited some of that from him. He even built a little collection of histories and memoirs and fiction in Ukrainian that I too eventually read. My mother is different; she grew up in Kyiv, her mother wrote for literary magazines, and her father worked as an editor for a newspaper. My mother was not only a very good student in high school, but also danced in the school folk-dance troupe. After graduation they went on a trip to Cuba to represent Russian-Ukrainian culture. In the waiting lounge in London, she slipped away from her minders and presented herself as a defector to the first local security person she saw. Who knows what she was thinking, but this impulsive step changed everyone's life. Her parents were punished for bringing up such a bad apple and soon lost their jobs. They barely survived. Her father took to drinking and died a few years later. Her mother rediscovered her Jewish roots and became a Zionist activist, with the result that she was harassed by the authorities for much of the rest of her life.

"'My mother was all alone in Britain without anything but her brilliant graduation degree, a knowledge of folk dance, a smattering of English, her intelligence, her dazzling good looks, and a luxurious fur coat. This was what she was wearing when she defected, although why she would have taken it to Cuba is a mystery. She still has that coat.'

"From the way he talked about her, I could sense that he was very close to his mother. I put my other hand on his. 'Let's go to the Castle Hill,' I said, 'and look at the city from up high while the sun is out. It's too beautiful to stay indoors. You can tell me the rest on the way.'

"'Well, there is not that much more to tell,' he said as we headed out. 'My mother was interrogated by MI5 and was helped to enroll at Birkbeck College, where she took evening classes while working at odd jobs during the day. Her case caused quite a stir at the time, because of how she defected and her good looks. Even today, if you google Olga Orionova, you will find accounts of the event, but nothing else about the rest of her life. Her brief brush with the media made her want to keep the rest of her life as private as possible. I think she was terrified that the KGB would come after her. This was London in the mid-1960s, and things were beginning to roll; pop music and the Beatles and miniskirts, and she was just 18 and all on her own in a completely new and different world.

"'God only knows how she managed those first few months. Then someone took her under his wing. She would never tell us who it was, or how he found her, although I think he must have been among her interrogators or had seen her file. In any case, he was an older man, a lord or other member of the nobility, with political contacts and influence. He promised to help get her parents out of the Soviet Union and, meanwhile, set her up quite comfortably in Bloomsbury. She fell madly in love with him, but he was married and had a reputation to protect. She told me that after a while she started drinking, which didn't do much for her studies. Their relationship went on for three years and she became increasingly miserable.

"'She had learned to drive, and this lord would occasionally let her use his sports car. That way she could get out of town when he could not be with her, which became increasingly often, and he'd get her off his hands for a while. Right after she graduated, when she was beset by panic about what to do next and the lord did not have time to see her, she drove out to the Cotswolds, and from there to Gloucester. Somehow, she ended up at the garage where my father worked. The car must have needed some serious repairs, because they ended up spending a fair amount of time together. She knew some Ukrainian, although her best language was Russian, and he still spoke the Ukrainian he had learned as a child on the farm. It must have seemed to them like they had something in common. My father was quite handsome and athletic when he was young, and she was just gorgeous. I can show you some photos from that time. So, the car of that child-abusing lord, as I have always thought of him, brought her to my father.

"It did not take her long to dump the lord and marry my father, even though I think that creep actually broke her heart. In the end, he had done nothing to help her parents. She never saw her father again. She was finally able to visit Kyiv in 1991, when her mother was 70 and quite ill. By then my mother had trained as a teacher and was working in a local elementary school in Gloucester, the one where she was recently appointed headmistress; not a mean accomplishment for someone who is still treated as somewhat exotic because of her funny accent and foreign mannerisms.'

"'This sounds like a beautiful love story,' I said, trying not to sound too cynical.

"I thought that I had no such story to tell," Tali wrote, "having never had a father and with my mother going in and out of the loony bin. We were now climbing the hill and I asked Andriy to stop and rest for a moment on one of the benches along the path.

"'It should have been a beautiful story,' he said. 'My father still adores my mother; he gave her a home, worked really hard, and eventually managed to take over the garage. He has a few workers of his own now, mostly from Poland. But I don't think they ever really had anything in common, apart from me.'

"I couldn't quite tell if he was being flippant or sad. 'My father was always a blue-collar worker,' said Andriy, 'and he likes it that way; he enjoys fixing things with his hands. But my mother wanted to be much more than a wife and a mother and the teacher of a bunch of unruly working-class brats. I think she had a happy childhood and that her decision to defect was more of an impulsive act of youthful rebellion. She was sure her parents would somehow manage to follow her or that she would be able to go back. In some ways she kept waiting for them to come and they never did. She has always been quite lonely. She had this idea of finding some more sophisticated friends, people who could talk about art and literature. But my parents' social circle was made up of people like my father; blokes who went to the pub after work, and on Saturdays their wives would join them and have half a pint of shandy. Every once in a while, they would go on a picnic or to the pictures. I think for her it was and still is a very boring life. You have no idea how happy she was when she heard that I was going to Oxford. It was as if I had done what she had always dreamed of, as if I would be earning my DPhil just for her. This was one of the few things my mother and grandfather agreed was a great achievement.'

"We were now almost at the top of the hill. We could see Lviv spread out below, the domes and steeples of its many churches gleaming in the sun. 'So, you were the realization of her dream,' I said.

"'Yes, and of my grandfather's. He never stopped talking about having a grandchild at Oxford. My father didn't think much of it, though. I mean, he helped and all that, but I think he would have rather seen me doing what he considers a man's job, not hobnobbing with all those fancy Oxford people. And in truth, I was very ambivalent about it all. I went to a pretty mediocre comprehensive school in Gloucester, and had good grades, which was not very difficult there. Then I went to Sheffield University, which I quite liked at the beginning but had tired of by the time I left. You know, Sheffield is in the heart of old industrial Britain, now quite dismal, but the university was full of smart middle-class kids.

"'They were constantly going on about this or that; the newest theory, existentialism, deconstruction, postmodernism, Derrida and Lacan,

Foucault and Kristeva. Half of the time I had no idea what they were talking about and the other half I thought they were just putting on airs. This was not why I had gone to university, and suddenly I realized that I had never asked myself the point of the whole thing. I felt so out of place and so mediocre and ignorant and simple-minded, just not part of that whole crowd. I think they also felt that about me and treated me like some sort of primitive plant; something that either had to be carefully cultivated or pulled up and discarded, very rough around the edges, so to speak. They were all so concerned with authenticity and meaning, desperately arguing that the world is absurd and the past unknowable. They appeared to me so smug, spouting all this verbiage while planning a comfortable life ensconced in some stuffy study, preaching the gospel of ambivalence to another generation of befuddled students.

"'The only authentic person who knew where he came from and who he was, who could actually take something broken and fix it, was my father in his shop. He put on no airs and didn't try to be what he was not. The same was true of his mates. So why was I trying to be someone I was not and could never really be? I felt just like my mother, who is still considered an outsider after all these years. What was it about me and about her that meant we were always trying to fit where we didn't actually belong? In any case, once I got my first degree I went back to Gloucester and told my dad that I wanted to work in his shop for a while. He was very happy, I mean, he didn't say he was happy, but I could tell he was. My mother, on the other hand, was totally despondent, thinking that I was throwing my future in the bin. And that was how it was for four years. I worked long hours in the garage, hung out with the local kids, went to the pub, and tried not to think about anything else, not even to read. It was my grandfather who finally got to me and persuaded me to apply to Oxford.'

"It was getting colder now, and we decided to walk back to the hotel through a small park. Andriy had put his arm around me," she wrote,

72

"and I suddenly felt very close to him. I thought that we never know the other person, we never know ourselves without narrating some version of who we are to another. I wondered whether what he was telling me was my story, the story that he could only tell me, and that if he told it to anyone else it would be a different story, told by a different person. He still knew almost nothing about me, which I thought was a good thing. I asked him how his grandfather had changed his mind.

"'You know,' Andriy said, 'my grandfather is a strange character. On one hand, he is just an old peasant, and speaks about himself in that way, as if that was what he was always destined to remain and that's all there is to it. But as I told you, he also got into the habit of reading, not just anything, but about where he came from. He was basically self-taught and always aware of it. I think he was in awe about people who really know, like historians who can write what actually happened, or novelists who can reconstruct a social reality of the past that takes their readers into a world that no longer exists. I also think that somewhere deep in him, although he never conceded it, he had hoped to soar higher, to study more and to understand better that world he left as a young man. So, for him, my going to Oxford was something very purposeful. My mother wanted me to have the career she never had, but he wanted me to go and study what he could never understand. But he didn't put it precisely this way to me.

"'You need to learn and tell others who we are,' he told me. 'We don't exist in history because no one researched us, no one wrote about us. We passed through the past like the shadows of clouds. We need a historian of our own, who will write our past so that we too can be proud of our history. That is more important than changing a gearbox. This is the story of the people you come from, and you have a duty to write it.'

"'I thought to myself that my grandfather was a strange old bird. This ancient peasant with parchment-like skin, rough, still powerful, hands and narrow, blue eyes, which were now fixed on me as if he was trying to penetrate my soul, wanted me to undertake this mission for him.

"'I don't think I can accomplish all that,' I told him, 'but I am getting a bit tired of repairing broken gearboxes.'

"'You should leave that to your father,' he said. 'He likes that and is good at it. You are too smart for that kind of job, like your mother. You should study, not waste your time in this place. And one day you'll be able to explain what happened to us, why so much blood was shed and whether it was all worth it.'

"I applied and was accepted to St. Antony's College to write a thesis on the origins and radicalization of Ukrainian nationalism in Eastern Galicia. It was not easy, especially at the beginning. I was always scared that the thin veneer of my education would wear off if I talked too long or had one too many beers. Then I'd be exposed for what I was, the grandson of a peasant who got off the boat lying about his past. I was haunted by my grandfather. I think my father was too, but he turned his back on the old man, whereas I was attracted to him like a moth.

"'In truth, I never entirely believed him. I always had a sense that with his peasant cunning, he was hiding something behind that wrinkly grin; something that despite all the stories he told, all his tall tales of battles fought and lost, of surviving winter in the forest and stripping boots off dead NKVD men, of living off boiled roots and roasted rats, he would not and perhaps could not tell. I was and still am afraid to ask, even though that was precisely why he wanted me to study, as if he had always wanted me to uncover the truth he could not divulge. Over these past few years, I have learned a huge amount about the world in which he grew up, all the possible lives he might have lived, and the choices he might have made. But I know as little today as I knew before I set out on this journey about what he really experienced, what he really did during the war. For that reason, I thought that maybe, if I went to his village, I would find some clue.

Then I would know what to ask him, and get him to confess what I now believe has always weighed heavily on his conscience.'

"The next day we set out early to Zaklots," Tali wrote. "I had read the town's memorial book and a few other essays, including some of yours. It was a long drive, over five hours, not just because the town is remote but also because the roads were so bad. Some of the potholes were more like huge craters in the middle of the road. The Lada smelled of gasoline and we had to keep the windows slightly open, even though it had turned colder and there were patches of snow and ice by the side of the road. 'This is March in Ukraine,' Andriy chortled. 'I always heard stories about it.'

"I wrapped myself in my coat and looked out at the bleak landscape.

"'It's beautiful here in June,' Andriy said.

"'I don't think I'll stay that long,' I answered. 'I'll come again in a few years when they've fixed the roads. Where are we going to spend the night?'

"'We'll have to go on to Ivano-Frankivsk,' he said. 'Zaklots has no hotels now. Before the war there were three hotels in the town, at least two of them owned by Jews. Now we'd be lucky to find something to eat and a public toilet.'

"A big concrete sign with square Cyrillic letters by the side of the road announced that we were approaching our destination. 'Porushennya,' it said. The road wound around a little hill and the town came into view."

YEVHEN

"From a distance it looked quite pretty," Tali wrote. "The town lay in a little valley, through which a serpentine steam cut its way, dividing it into a more and a less populated part. Several hills surrounded the town, each with its own distinct features. As we drove in, crossing a little bridge, I could see one hill on the right, dotted with what appeared from the distance to be scattered tombstones. On the left, I glimpsed a small white church with a blue onion dome. A large wooden cross was planted in the ground next to it.

"'What does that say?' I asked Andriy, pointing to the sign on the gate in front of the church.

"'Remember our martyrs,' he said.

"It was cold, and the few people on the street were wrapped up in shabby coats. Some were wearing fur hats, the flaps covering their ears. An elegant baroque tower loomed in front of us, partly covered by scaffolding. Behind it I could see the ruins of a castle on top of another hill.

"We parked in the main square next to the tower, which I now realized was the town's famous city hall, stripped of much of its ornamentation. Its facade was crumbling, and the sealed windows looked out to a massive, Soviet-style statue of a stocky man with a long moustache.

"'Our national poet,' Andriy said, carefully locking the car.

"Across the square on our left, I could see another bridge, and beyond it a large, sprawling edifice topped by a steeple.

"'This must be the Basilian Monastery,' Andriy said.

"The monastery stood on a slope leading up to another, densely forested hill. My feet were freezing. We crossed the square, and a large, rather squat, church came into view, painted white and cream with a light-blue roof and steeple.

"'This one looks Roman Catholic,' muttered Andriy.

"We approached the massive iron gate, but it was locked. A tall, elderly man approached us and said something in Ukrainian.

"'He is asking whether we want to go in,' Andriy explained.

"'You speak English,' the man said.

"I nodded.

"'You come from where?' he asked.

"'Israel.'

"'I can speak a little Hebrew,' he said in Hebrew, 'un a bissel Yiddish.'

"'My friend doesn't know these languages,' I said, 'so let's stick to English.'

"'I can open the gate for you,' the man said, pulling out a bunch of large keys from his pocket. 'But let me introduce myself first. I am Yevhen Pasichnyk.'

"We introduced ourselves and followed him into the church, which felt even colder than outdoors.

"Yevhen invited us to sit down with him in one of the pews in the back of the church. What a strange apparition, I thought. He seemed to have materialized from nowhere. Judging by his eagerness to guide us, I thought he might simply be looking for some extra income.

"'This old Roman Catholic church,' Yevhen explained, 'had been abandoned under the communists. They even used it as a storage space, but since the fall of the regime, it has been restored, thanks especially to its old priest, Father Motyka, who returned from a 40-year exile and has even reestablished a small congregation.' Yevhen pointed at the magnificent altar, adding that its most precious sculptures by a famous 18th-century artist were now exhibited in the municipal museum of Ternopil. His dark hair was streaked with gray, but sitting right next to him, his face seemed younger than I had initially thought. There was something odd about the way he carried himself and spoke in stilted, formal English.

"'How come you know Hebrew?' I asked.

"'I went to school in Ternopil, and my landlady spoke Hebrew, so I asked her to teach me. She also knew Yiddish. She had lived in this town during the war and was saved by the man she later married. They went to Israel for a few years but returned here to live in Ternopil.'

"'But why would you want to learn Hebrew?' I asked.

"'This was a Jewish town; before the war only Jews lived in the center. No one here knows or wants to talk about this. So I decided to write the history of Zaklots,' Yevhen said, using the town's Jewish name.

"'Do you teach history?'

"'No, I work in the municipality. History is my hobby. Apart from those few years in Ternopil, I have lived here all my life with my mother. She was ill for a long time, and I took care of her. Recently she died, and I have more time to research the city.'

"'I am so sorry for your loss', I said.

"'I can take you around and show you some sites,' Yevhen offered, already back on his feet and marching toward the entrance to the church.

"We first walked up the steep hill to the castle ruins overlooking the town. Then we descended back into the main part of the town, which betrayed decades of neglect and poverty; the once handsome houses looked shabby, the gaping spaces between them, likely due to war damage, plugged with shoddily constructed and ugly new buildings. People holding plastic bags were rummaging through the merchandise displayed on the street; small piles of used clothes, banged-up pots, plastic dishes, old bicycle parts, rubber tubes, and rusting cutlery. I recalled descriptions in the town's memorial book of its vibrant prewar marketplace, its stalls mostly populated by Jews selling their own wares and the produce they bought in the surrounding villages.

"As we turned a corner, Yevhen drew our attention to one of the buildings. 'This is where the German gendarmes were based during the war,' he said. 'The Judenrat was also quartered nearby. And the residence of the Landkommissar, who was the German civilian administrator at the time, was in a house that faced the square, which had windows that looked out to the river and the monastery on one side and to the city hall and the Jewish cemetery hill on the other. That house was destroyed in the fighting in 1944, but I saw photographs of it from before the war. I can take you to visit the cemetery later if you have time.'

"He was walking with quick, small steps, his long coat trailing behind him. He spoke rapidly, as if he had rehearsed everything numerous times and had just been waiting for the opportunity to impart his knowledge to a visitor. To me, in fact, because he displayed no interest in Andriy, who was, after all, Ukrainian, or at least appeared to be, and for that reason was not expected to have any interest in the town's Jewish past. All this time I was thinking what my mother would have made of all this had she come here. Would she have been able to find her way around these sad, dilapidated streets? Now, as I write this, I think that had you been there with me, you might have said to him, 'I too am writing a history of this town.' But you were not there, at least not then," she wrote.

"We were now crossing the bridge to the monastery.

"To our right, Yevhen pointed out a two-story building with a walled-off courtyard on the opposite side of the road. 'This is the Ukrainian police station,' he said. 'This is where they held the Jews they rounded up before taking them to the pits.' We did not stop to look at the freshly painted entrance. 'They would then lead them up the same road we are taking now,' he continued.

"We were marching uphill and then turned onto a path leading toward the forest. The ground was covered with snow. I could no longer feel my toes, but this did not seem the right time to complain. The snow creaked under our feet and our breaths formed little clouds of steam. As we plunged ever deeper into the forest, I was suddenly overwhelmed with anxiety. Who was this Yevhen? Why is he taking us here? We know nothing about him. Maybe he knows Andriy? Am I being led into some trap? I looked around but all I could see was more and more trees. I was close to panic, my heart pounding, my breath shallow, my knees wobbly.

"'Here we are,' Yevhen called out from among the trees. 'Come here!'

"In the distance, a single tombstone appeared in a small clearing. Coming closer, I saw that it was carved with words in Cyrillic and a Star of David.

"'This is the site of the first mass grave,' Yevhen said. 'It's hard to see now, because of the snow, but in the summer, one can clearly identify where the ground is uneven. There are thousands of bodies buried here. The graves are shallow, and during the thaw, bones surface. Every year dog owners report finding human bones in their kennels. But no one speaks about where they come from.'

"Later on, back in the square, I said that I simply had to warm up a little and eat something," Tali wrote. "We went to a pizza place down the street.

"'This is the only place in town where you can use the toilet,' Yevhen said. 'There is another restaurant, but I don't recommend it. Where are you staying tonight?'

"'In Ivano-Frankivsk,' Andriy said.

"'Rightly so,' Yevhen responded. 'We have one hotel here, but it's for truckers and not a place you would enjoy.'

"Again, I noticed that he looked only at me.

"'My mother lived here during the war,' he said after we had sat down at the only table in the tiny restaurant and I returned from the very basic toilet in the backyard, feeling much better. 'She told me that there were some wonderful restaurants here before the Soviets came in 1939, but they nationalized them. The best restaurant and hotel were owned a by a Jew named Aberdam. They were featured in the Polish tourist guide before the war. I still have a copy of it. When the Germans came two years later, they handed these restaurants over to Poles and Ukrainians, but they only served the Germans and a few of their favorite locals. The Germans came here with their wives and children or took local mistresses. They especially liked Aberdam's old restaurant. During the war, it was owned by Piotr Siewiński, a Pole and a decent fellow. His father was the headmaster of an elementary school for decades and died just before the war. Piotr fled in 1944, when the Ukrainian insurgents started killing Poles. By then most of the Jews were already dead. I think he ended up somewhere in Silesia. He was lucky to survive; a lot of blood was shed here.

"'In any case, when the Germans were here, Siewiński took care to supply them with the best food and alcohol. They had a refined taste when it came to drink, especially the members of the local administration. They would not settle for local beer like the gendarmes. My mother had a Jewish classmate who worked for the local officials. She told her that the Jewish Council had to supply them with everything; food, alcohol, clothes, furniture, boots, and medical and dental services, and that all they got in return was the promise to be kept alive a few more days. Sarah, her Jewish friend, was fluent in German, and in addition to administrative work, she was also a babysitter to the daughter of the head of the post office, a German. At times Sarah would also go shopping for his wife and do her hair, because she had trained as a hairdresser during Soviet times.

"'Siewiński would arrange for supplies from Jews, but at least he paid them, although much less than he should have. They managed to find for him all kind of rarities; sardines in olive oil and red wine from Portugal, fancy liquors from France, and special beers from Belgium. The Germans loved his place. When there were roundups, they would draw the restaurant's heavy curtains to muffle the gunshots and screams from the streets and block out the sight of what was going on so they could keep eating and drinking.

"'My mother told me that one day the director of the post office and his wife were having drinks there with the wife of the train station director, and Sarah was at their home with the child. They should have known a roundup was planned, but perhaps it was more of a local initiative by the town's gendarmerie, not one of those major events where the Security Police would drive in from their headquarters in the nearby town of Barnów. You may have heard of this place; Barnów was a big center of Hasidism before the war. Someone must have denounced Sarah to the police, or perhaps the gendarmes resented the local administrators, who thought of themselves as socially more refined than the crass and often drunk middle-aged policemen of the town, and decided to punish them by taking away their domestic help. In any event, they burst into the apartment, which was on the third floor of the building overlooking the bridge. Later, Sarah was found with a crushed skull on the sidewalk. Either she jumped, or they threw her out. They left the child there, and the parents found her in a state of shock when they returned a couple of hours later.'

"The pizza was terrible," Tali wrote, "but we were hungry and had no other alternative. The young woman at the counter, standing only a few feet from us, did not appear interested in our conversation, though there were no other customers. We drank our coffees and left.

"'There is just enough time to see the Jewish cemetery,' Yevhen said, 'but it's getting late, so I can drive you. My car is nearby.'

"We piled into his noisy little car and headed down the main street, passing the small Greek Catholic church with the large wooden cross and turning left onto an unpaved road heading to the top of the hill. I sat in the back. The two men in the front were exchanging a few words in Ukrainian. I was trying to digest everything I had heard and to somehow connect it to my mother's fantasies of paradise, the hometown where she had never lived, but I felt numb and nauseous from the cold and the pizza. You know, I have never really processed this trip until now. Here I am, in pristine New Zealand, on the other side of the world, trying to articulate what I experienced by writing to you. For the life of me I don't quite know why, but I guess you are also part of this story in some way, and I suspect that in your own objective, analytical way you are as broken as me.

"At the top of the hill Yevhen pulled over to the side of the road and turned off the engine. To our left, the town was spread out below, its 18th-century edifices bathed in the soft late afternoon light; the little white and blue Greek Catholic church, the squat white and yellow Roman Catholic church, the monastery across the river at the foot of the hill with its unmarked mass graves, and the ruins of the medieval castle etched against the sky. The Zaklots memorial book describes the town as brimming with synagogues, ranging from the vast Groysse Shil to the innumerable tiny *shtibelach* that dotted the Jewish neighborhood before the war. None of them survived. But from where we stood, the town appeared unscathed, as if the extraction of its entrails had somehow left it still whole.

"I turned around and realized that we were standing at the edge of a cemetery, strewn with colorful piles of garbage; plastic containers, empty cans, broken beer bottles and rotting bits of food—the discarded leftovers of a destitute community that could no longer be recycled and reused. Gingerly watching their step, Yevhen and Andriy headed toward a heap of broken stones, next to which a half full barrow had been left. The Hebrew letters and decorative motifs carved on these fragments of tombstones were still visible. 'Abraham, son of Elazar, seized before his time and ripped from life, his soul has ascended to heaven, here buried in an underground tomb,' one fragment read, but it no longer stood by its grave, and the grave was no longer marked by its stone.

"'Someone is preparing to cart these off,' Yevhen said nonchalantly, as if there was nothing peculiar about this decimation of a community's last remnants. Looking around, I could see that the entire hill was dotted with crooked, misshapen, half-fallen, or decapitated tombstones. They looked like a crowd of people left waiting for someone who has been greatly delayed; some erect and looking into the distance, others sitting on the ground, tired and dispirited; and some, so beaten down by time, the weather, and their neighbors' violence, that they were reduced to nothing more than mutilated stumps. I realized that my great-grandmother must be buried here, but the thought of looking for her on this hill of fragmented tombstones amidst piles of garbage seemed absurd. These pieces could not be put together again, could not be matched with the bodies they had once commemorated, giving them names and faces and voices, letting them tell the stories of their forgotten lives and deaths.

"Yevhen was already leading us to another part of the hill. 'This is the mass grave,' he said, pointing at the uneven ground in front of us. 'Some 3,000 people are buried here, killed in May and June 1943, when the town was declared free of Jews. My mother remembered that day very well. They were shooting all day long and everyone could hear it. Some of the boys from the town went up the hill to see for themselves. Women were holding their babies, old men were standing next to small children, waiting for their turn to walk into the pits that were already filled with bodies, and then they were shot by the police. My mother told me about the local police sergeant, a middle-aged man with children in Germany, who used some of the condemned for target practice.

"'The Jews were not crying or begging for mercy. Some mothers were stroking their children's heads and reassuring them as they awaited their turn, forced to see those who went before being shot over the writhing bodies of families and friends. I sometimes wondered whether she had gone there herself to look or whether she was just repeating what others told her, but I never dared to ask. They only stopped the shooting when it got dark. By then the German security police, the local gendarmes, and the Ukrainian police that surrounded the site were all drunk. The Jewish Council had been ordered to provide a sufficient amount of vodka and cigarettes, and when it was all over the Germans climbed into their vehicles and drove back to their base and the Ukrainian auxiliary police marched back to the city. They were singing about how they'd slaughtered the Jews and what they'd do next to the Poles. Once the Jews were all dead, they did indeed begin killing the Poles, but this time on their own because the Germans had no interest in this. But the Poles fought back and killed many of our people in return.'

"We stood on top of that pit and looked over to the other peak—both hills stuffed with Jewish corpses. A sudden blast of wind from the valley made me so cold that I began trembling. I told Andriy that we really must head back to the car before it got dark.

"'Do you know where the Great Synagogue was located?' I asked Yevhen as we drove back to the main square.

"'It was just behind the square,' he answered, pointing in the direction of an open market, where peddlers had set up stalls under metal and tarpaulin roofs. 'It was demolished after the war.'

"We were about to turn into the square, where Andriy's car was parked, when we ran into a procession and had to wait for it to pass. In the front, an old Russian pickup truck was carrying a coffin on its open cargo bed. Behind it two men were marching, one carrying the blue and yellow flag of Ukraine and the other a red and black banner. A long row of people stretched out behind them, all the way back to the monastery across the river.

"'That's the flag of the Ukrainian Insurgent Army,' Yevhen said. 'Red for the blood of the martyrs, black for the soil of the homeland. The dead man was a member.'

"'Like your grandfather,' I said to Andriy.

"'Yes, like my grandfather.'

"For the first time, Yevhen looked directly at Andriy and muttered something in Ukrainian. We parked in the square and thanked our guide. 'You are quite a remarkable man,' I said, almost adding, 'for such a desolate town.'

"He smiled weakly. Suddenly he seemed quite lost and much older. Perhaps he was thinking about how his mother was gone and that he had no one to go back to at home. He left his car in the square, and we could see him walking slowly toward the bridge, a little bent and limping.

"'I should have asked him how far along he is in his history of Zaklots,' I said.

"'I bet he talks more than he writes,' Andriy responded.

"I wondered if that was the young historian speaking dismissively of an old storyteller, or a young Ukrainian embarrassed by this peculiar old relic and miffed by the interest I had taken in him.

"'What did he say to you?' I asked.

"'Just now? Nothing important.'

"We got into the car and drove off. I was quite drained and slept most of the way to Ivano-Frankivsk."

MYRYN

"We stayed at the well-appointed Stanislau Hotel.

"'Stanislau was the German version of the town's original name—it's Stanisławów in Polish and Stanyslaviv in Ukrainian—before it became Ivano-Frankivsk under the Soviets in the 1960s,' Andriy explained to me, adding that 'it's a rather curious choice, because this new name was meant to honor the author Ivan Franko, one of the most influential promoters of Ukrainian nationalism at the turn of the last century. My grandfather has most of his novels in his little collection and admires him almost as much our national poet Taras Shevchenko, that chap with the long moustache you saw in front of the city hall in Porushennya, after whom my father is named. Franko was also pretty antisemitic.'

"As we drove into the city in the dark, I observed shabby suburbs and an impressive city center with wide boulevards and handsome 19th-century houses. Building works and other improvements were going on throughout. It even occurred to me that I might want to include this city in my next tourist guide. As Andriy checked us in, I leafed through the attractively printed hotel brochure, available also in German and English. It explained to guests that this formerly private mansion, which had belonged to the affluent Wahrman family before World War II, had recently been purchased by an Austrian hotel chain and meticulously restored to its former glory. The lobby displayed wood panels and bright white walls with discreetly lit framed photographs and lithographs of old Austrian Galicia.

"'Everyone is trying to claim a bit of Ukraine to themselves,' Andriy commented, as we sat down to dinner at the hotel restaurant, while I mentally considered the irony of spending the night in a Jewish villa renovated by the descendants of those who may have murdered its original owners. We were very hungry, and the staff agreed to serve us what was left even though they had closed the kitchen. It seemed like tourism had not yet picked up in the city; as far as we could tell we were the only guests. Andriy had beer with his Wiener schnitzel and fries. I ordered some local fish and white wine.

"'A strange character, that Yevhen,' said Andriy. 'I wonder where he got all that information.'

"'He said his mother told him.'

"'I don't know, there was something odd about him. I can't even tell if he's really from there. He might have just come up with the whole thing.'

"I was beginning to feel uncomfortable. 'You think he invented the entire story about the murder of the Jews in the town?' I asked.

"'No, of course not,' Andriy said defensively, 'but he just seemed to know a lot of details for someone who wasn't there himself. Maybe he embellished a bit.'

"'I don't think that the massacre of women and children can be called embellishment,' I said.

"Something was happening to me that I could not control. 'I read about this in the town's memorial book,' I continued, trying to calm myself down.

"'Well, you know, those are not the most reliable historical sources,' Andriy said calmly, making his way through his schnitzel.

"I looked down at my fish, overcome with nausea. I tried to block those images from my mind; those mothers waiting patiently, holding their babies, about to be driven down the pit and shot on a mound of writhing corpses. I began to cry silently. My whole body was shaking.

"'I'm sorry,' Andriy said. 'Have some wine.'

"I looked at him in horror. What was I doing in this place with this man? Why was I there? Andriy was speaking to me, but I could no longer hear him. The old fear that I might end up like my mother suddenly overwhelmed me. I got up and went to our room without touching the food. I got under the blanket without taking off my clothes and curled up around a pillow. In the morning I found myself in Andriy's arms. My pillow was still wet. I must have been crying most of the night.

"We set out right after breakfast. Andriy was quiet and said nothing about my outburst the previous night. Perhaps he was tense about finally going to his ancestral village. I was a little embarrassed about my crying fit. It was not like me at all. I am usually in control and take care of others. I looked out of the window, feeling the cool breeze on my face, fighting the smell of gasoline. This must be one of the most polluting engines in the universe, I thought, listening to the rattle from under the hood. On the outskirts of the city we were stopped by the police. An officer asked Andriy to roll down his window and hand over his papers. We had driven straight through a traffic circle. The officer was unconvinced by Andriy's observation that there were no visible indications that this was in fact a traffic circle. After walking back and forth to his patrol car, the officer finally let us go. Andriy pointed out that the banknote of 500 Hryvna that he kept with his papers for precisely this kind of eventuality was no longer there.

"Driving east, it took us less than an hour to reach the Dniester. I must have been sleeping when we had crossed it the previous day. On the long, single-lane bridge, we found ourselves behind an extremely slow truck. It was a wide river, and I had plenty of time to observe it. When we finally reached the other bank, there was a line of cars awaiting their turn to cross in the other direction. The truck in front accelerated past the horse-drawn wagon that had slowed us down. A large woman with a colorful kerchief over her head sat behind the man driving the cart. That must be how my ancestors got around these parts not so long ago, I thought.

"Less than a mile from the bridge we turned right onto a dirt road and spent the next hour bumping along it, driving in and out of patches of forest and farmland, with fleeting glimpses of the Dniester to our right. Finally, a rusty metal sign indicated that we had arrived. Throughout the drive we had hardly exchanged a word. Andriy drove slowly into the village, a single street of small houses on either side with fields stretching out behind them. Andriy rolled down his window and spoke with an old man walking down the street. The man became quite animated. Then he got into the backseat and began giving Andriy directions. Our path took us toward a patch of forest separating the village from the river. In front of us were the ruins of a mansion surrounded by tall trees.

The roof had caved in, and the vegetation had taken over the interior.

"I think one of your books has similar photographs of abandoned synagogues invaded by nature," Tali wrote. "But this was no synagogue. It made me think of Macondo in *One Hundred Years of Solitude.*

"'Our friend, Mykola, tells me that this is where the Polish estate owner and her sons lived when he was a boy,' said Andriy. 'My grandfather worked here as a stableboy.'

"He stopped the car and we got out. There was a wonderful smell in the air, of pine, soil, and food being cooked. Across the dirt road from the mansion were a few low houses.

"'This must have been the estate manager's house,' Andriy said when we reached the spot.

"The houses were all abandoned. 'Why is no one living here?' I asked. The old man had stayed by the car, and I could now hear him calling out to us. I turned back and saw him pointing at one of the houses and gesturing, passing a finger over his throat, and I could not quite tell whether he was grinning or expressing horror. 'What is he saying?' I asked Andriy.

"'He says that there was a murder here and people are afraid to come to this spot. They say it brings bad luck.'

"'Who was murdered? When did it happen?'

"Mykola lit a cigarette, coughed, and spat on the ground.

"'Ask him,' I insisted.

"'We should go back to the village,' Andriy said. 'I don't think he likes being here.'

"'Let me just walk around for a bit. This is where my family came from,' I said.

"Andriy looked surprised.

"'I thought they came from Porushennya.'

"'My grandfather, Adolf, was born and grew up right here on the estate. As apparently did yours.'

"It had become warmer, and one could almost sense that spring was around the corner. We walked over to the larger house in the yard, which seemed to have withstood the ravages of time better than the mansion. I tried the door. It was unlocked and we walked slowly into the dark interior of an almost empty room.

"'They were afraid of ghosts,' said Andriy, 'but they took all the furniture.'

"There was a large fireplace at one end. Above it hung a large axe with a beautifully decorated handle.

"'That's weird,' Andriy said. 'You would have thought that the peasants wouldn't have left this behind.'

"'I don't like this place,' I said. 'It feels creepy. Let's get out.'

"There was a gust of wind and the door slammed shut. All I could see was the blade of the axe shining on the wall. I held Andriy's arm. 'Let's go,' I insisted. We made our way back to the car, where Mykola was patiently waiting, smoking his cigarette.

"'Hey, look!' I called out. A beautiful large butterfly was hovering over the bushes by the car.

"'A harbinger of spring,' Andriy answered.

"We drove back to the village where Mykola insisted that we join him for a glass of vodka. We sat in the tiny, enclosed porch of his house, which seemed to have only one large room. He was a wiry man with a deeply creased face and bright blue eyes. He smelled of sweat, alcohol, and tobacco. His wife, a large woman, brought out a tray with vodka and glasses, a loaf of bread, and a jar of honey. The sun streamed in through a filter of finely woven curtains, casting geometrical shapes on the table. Outside, chickens pecked in the yard. We raised our glasses.

"'I told them that your family once lived here,' said Andriy. 'They are very happy that you have come to visit.'

"I thanked them and asked if they remember my family.

"'No,' Andriy said. 'They were little children during the war. People in the village say that the Polish owners always had a Jew to manage their estate, but just before the war the Jews left and the estate was managed by someone from the Carpathians, a Hutsul.'

"'Do they know what happened there?'

"Mykola poured another round, but Andriy refused. 'I told him that I have a long drive ahead,' he said.

"Mykola lit a cigarette and talked for a while. I did not want to interrupt him and waited until he finished.

"'We really must leave, I don't want to drive in the dark on these lousy roads,' said Andriy. 'I'll tell you what he said in the car.'

"I gave Mykola a 20-dollar bill and after refusing a couple of times he took it and thanked me profusely.

"'He is blessing your family with good health and longevity,' said Andriy.

"As we left the house, we saw that neighbors had gathered on the street, eager to watch these unlikely visitors. We got into the car and drove off, taking with us Mykola's lingering odor.

"'What did he tell you?' As we bumped along the dirt road, I felt lightheaded from the two shots of vodka.

"Andriy lowered his window a little more. 'It's getting warmer,' he said. 'But it'll probably get cold again. It doesn't really get consistently warm here until June.'

"'I guess that butterfly we saw won't stand much of a chance.'

"'A butterfly that size could live for a while.'

"How come you know so much about butterflies? Anyway, what did Mykola say?'

"'It's a horrible story,' he replied. 'Are you sure you want to hear it? Wasn't yesterday enough for you?'

"'Of course I want to hear. That's why I came here,' I said, a bit impatient with his patronizing tone.

"Andriy looked at me and smiled.

"'OK, but I thought we came here because of me.'

"'That's true. Did you ask him about your grandfather?'

"'He doesn't remember him. But my grandfather must have known about this event. Maybe that's why he didn't want to return to the village. Only he never told me about it.'

"'So, what happened?'

"'Andriy drove slowly, avoiding the potholes. We passed through another little village. A family of geese crossed the road and further ahead a little girl was leading a cow tied to a rope. The sun was now high and the shadows were getting shorter. To our left I caught glimpses of the Dniester. Everything looked as if it had remained unchanged since the beginning of time; the little houses with fruit trees in the front yard, the rolling farmland, the thick forest, the clear bright sky, the call of an occasional bird of prey, and the girl with a cow, they seemed like they had always been there.

"'Mykola told me that when the Germans came, the estate manager was a Hutsul whose name may have been Dmytro. The Polish owner, the Grafina, had died, and her sons had been deported by the Soviets. So Dmytro managed the estate, convinced that the sons would eventually come back to reclaim their property. But people in the village thought that this was just an excuse to take over the Poles' property. Dmytro had twins; two babies born just when the war began. The Soviets didn't mind him taking care of the farm, but for a while some of their men stayed in the mansion and messed it up. A bit later, when the Soviets fled from the Germans, they took with them most of the furniture and any valuables they could lay their hands on. No self-respecting German would have wanted to stay in this ransacked hole in the wall, so they left Dmytro and the village in peace.

"'The villagers were jealous of this Hutsul because he had so much land and livestock and could do whatever he wanted now that his

97

masters were gone. He never moved into the big house. A few months before the Soviets returned, a rumor started going around the village that Dmytro was hiding Jews on the estate. By then there had already been many killings of Jews in the area, but Myryn hadn't had any Jews since your great-grandfather sold his house to Dmytro. People heard about Jews being killed in nearby towns, but that had not affected their own lives, apart from the fact that since the Germans arrived, there were no Jews to buy their produce. Instead, they had to bring it to the market themselves, and market days in towns such as Porushennya were very different after the Germans came.

"'For a while thing were not so bad for the peasants, because Jews could not leave and were desperate for food. They would give the peasants whatever they had—expensive clothes, jewelry, gold, dollars —just for a jar of milk or a loaf of bread. The peasants did well; they had more money, better clothes, and nicer furniture and utensils. But then the Jews were all killed, and the Germans confiscated more and more produce and animals from the villages. Milk and cows and pigs and horses, eggs and wheat and potatoes, everything was taken by the Germans. People began going hungry. Some died from lack of food, others were rounded up and sent to work in Germany, which is what happened to my grandmother. There some of them died in Allied bombing raids.

"'In any case, it was after most of the nearby Jews had been killed that those rumors began circulating about Dmytro hiding Jews. People said, 'This cunning Hutsul, not only has he taken over the Polish estate, now he is making a fortune from the Jews he is hiding. He gets rich while we are getting poorer.' Other people worried that Dmytro's actions would put the whole village in jeopardy, and that all the houses would be burned down if the Germans or the Ukrainian police found out. But no one denounced him. In the end, Dmytro himself was at the root of what happened.'

"I was wondering," Tali wrote, "how Mykola could have conveyed so many details to Andriy during a conversation over a couple of shots of vodka. It appeared to me that Andriy knew much more about these events than he let on, and that he had only needed Mykola to verify details and show him the site. But it did not really matter to me. We were about to reach the main road, so Andriy stopped the car and consulted the map.

"'It's about three or four hours to Lviv from here,' he said. We got on the main road and started driving north.

"'In spring 1944,' Andriy continued, 'when the Germans began their retreat from the area, the Wehrmacht took up positions in many remote villages, and one company, Mykola was sure it was a Waffen-SS unit, established itself in the village. The company commander and his staff set themselves up in the old mansion. This was very dangerous. By now everyone knew that Dmytro was hiding a Jewish family under the Germans' noses, because just weeks before the SS arrived in the village, the Jewish family had been blessed with a baby; and the farm laborers who lived nearby could hear the cries of the woman who delivered it. They soon established that this family was made up of a young couple, a little girl, and a baby, who was delivered in Dmytro's house with the help of his wife.

"'The Jews were apparently hidden in a hayloft on the farm, and the villagers were terrified that sooner or later they would be found and the whole village would pay for it. They watched with horror as the Germans roamed around the yard, catching chickens, collecting eggs, and chatting with Oksana, Dmytro's beautiful wife. Everyone agreed that poor Dmytro was in a terrible bind. He could have chosen to expel the Jews from his property and deny any responsibility for them if they were found, but one of the villagers might have revealed to the Germans that he had been hiding Jews for a long time. He could have denounced the Jews to the Germans himself, but if they found out that he had previously hidden them they would have shot him and his family and burned down the property as a warning to any other Jew friends. Finally, he could simply kill the Jews himself, take whatever valuables they had kept as compensation for him after their liberation, and bury them secretly. But as the villagers now whispered to each other, this would be very hard for him, because it was rumored that these Jews were none other than old Szumer's daughter, who had grown up on the estate, and her husband. Some people even remembered this couple and their little girl visiting the estate shortly before the war, along with another young woman and her girl, who spoke a strange language that no one in the village had ever heard before.

"'No one knows exactly what happened but when the SS company relocated, the Hutsul and his family disappeared, and no trace was found of the Jewish family Dmytro had allegedly hidden in the barn. And since the Germans had burned down the barn as part of the scorched earth policy they implemented everywhere as they retreated, it was impossible to confirm whether there had in fact been any Jews there in the first place. Some people thought it was just a malicious rumor as no one had ever seen them. But then, why did the Hutsul take his family and flee, leaving behind all their property? Was he afraid of Jewish revenge now that the communists were returning?'

"I was sitting quite still in the car," Tali wrote, "looking straight ahead, unable to utter a word. I knew the story of my grandmother and mother's visit to Mierzyn just before the war. My mother always spoke about that visit as the happiest time of her life, and remembered little Judit as her best friend, although they only spent a few weeks together. She would always reminisce about how they played around the estate, went to bathe in the river, and how there were waves and waves of butterflies, so many, my mother would say, that she thought that she might have imagined them just because she had never seen anything like it since. The war changed everything, no butterflies could survive such inhumanity and destruction, she'd say.

"'And he never mentioned your grandfather?' I blurted out.

"'No, he couldn't remember him.'

"'What about the axe that we saw hanging there? Did he kill them with that axe?'

"'I asked him about it,' said Andriy, 'because it makes no sense that they would have left it there.'

"'And what did he say?'

"'He said that he had never seen any axe there,' replied Andriy. 'He had no idea what I was talking about. But then again, he also said that no one ever dared to go into that house, the villagers are sure that it's haunted.'

"'Who took all the furniture? Why is the house bare?'

"'I asked him about that too, but Mykola thinks that the Germans took everything with them. They stripped the entire country. They never worried about ghosts.'

"This is all that I can tell you about my trip to Ukraine 13 years ago," Tali wrote. "Andriy and I spent the rest of the time in Lviv, apart from taking the night train for a quick visit to Kyiv, a very different kind of city. I did go with him to Babi Yar, where his mother's grandparents were murdered. He told me that her parents were communist activists and were evacuated from the city before the Germans came, while her grandparents had stayed in Kyiv. No one thought that the Germans would harm old people. They shot 33,000 Jews in two days. But you know that of course. There is no trace of them. It is as if the earth opened its mouth and swallowed them whole. Even the ravine where they were shot has disappeared.

"We walked out of the metro station to the huge Soviet memorial and Andriy recited Yevtushenko's poem 'Babi Yar' in Russian and in English, which he wrote before that hideous monument was erected. It reads: 'No monument stands over Babi Yar, a sudden drop sheer as a makeshift tombstone, here I am filled with fear, today I am as ancient as all the Jewish people, now it seems I am a Jew.' I wondered what this poem meant to Andriy over a mass grave where a distant part of his family lay, written by a Russian who closed his poem with the statement, 'There is no Jewish blood in me.'

"I have not been in touch with Andriy since those two weeks in Ukraine, though I sometimes wonder what became of him. By now it's too late to reconnect, I think. What I experienced on that trip was very different from what I had expected, and it left a deep mark, although in truth it had no real effect on my life, and I avoided thinking about it until I met you at your father's shiva. Then everything seemed to come flooding back and it appeared as if what I had seen was some kind of a keyhole that I had not known existed. All I needed was a key to open the door and see a world that had always remained hidden; a world that was denied to me, living my life on the other side of that locked door in a narrow hallway of mutilated memories. But I had not found the key and could not open the door. I could only peep through the keyhole, and what I saw was so terrifying that I lost all taste for looking through keyholes ever again.

"I may stay in New Zealand. I like it here. It's a land with little memory and a beautiful, undisturbed geography. It's quiet, tranquil, and windy. Nothing sinks down, things are just blown away to the vast ocean on all sides. The green hills are dotted with white sheep. It is true that somewhere there must be vast slaughterhouses where all those little lambs are turned into neatly packaged and frozen meat and sent to the northern hemisphere, but you would never guess that had the thought not crossed your mind. If you stand at the tip of South Island, you can imagine that Antarctica is just beyond the horizon, and you feel literally at the end of the world. I like that feeling. Still, one of these days I may check on Andriy, simply to see what became of him. I do miss him sometimes. Be well and beware the history you study. I know you have been at it for a long time, but there is no telling what you might unravel and how it will affect you.

We think that as we grow older, we become more resilient. That is true, but not completely. We also become more fragile, more haunted by memories, by what we remember, what we fear we'll forget, and what unknown thing may resurface from a dark underground stream and drag us down the depths."

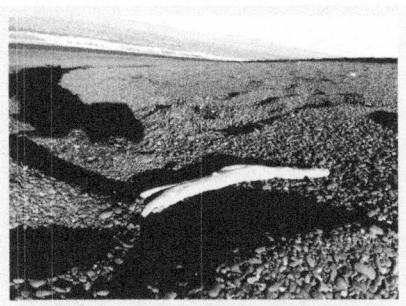

JANEK

It took me a few weeks to digest Tali's account of her visit to Ukraine. I had known a fair amount about what happened in Zaklots, so that came as less of a shock. But I did not know how Rochaleh and Max and Judit had died, nor that there had been another baby. I also could not help feeling that something in the story did not quite add up, though exactly what it was eluded me. What stuck in my mind was my mother's recounting of how Tova described her trip with Hannaleh to Mierzyn as a kind of last-minute visit to paradise. The way things had unfolded in that very same paradise seemed unspeakable. Everyone connected to these events was dead, even Hannaleh, if one could call her condition toward the end a fully conscious life. Then again, perhaps she chose the only life that was bearable to her.

Tali's account made me curious about the fate of Władek and Janek, the Grafina's sons. I asked a colleague at Stanford University to check whether the Hoover Institution had any materials on these two aristocrats in its vast collection of depositions by Poles. Many of these accounts are by people who were deported by the Soviets when they took over the region but, following Hitler's invasion, were allowed to establish a Polish military formation known as Anders' Army, which was eventually transferred via Iran and Palestine to fight against the Germans alongside the British forces in Europe. Władek, it turned out, had died in a Soviet camp. Fortunately, my colleague located and sent me a copy of the deposition submitted by his younger brother, Janek. As was typical of such accounts, Janek provided more personal information than the questionnaire asked for, including an intriguing encounter with my grandfather and great-uncle. This was Janek's story.

"I was born in Mierzyn on the Dniester in 1900. My father was killed in 1915 when serving as a colonel in the Polish Legions during World War I. I joined Haller's Blue Army and fought in the Polish-Ukrainian War of 1919 and in the Russo-Polish War of 1920. Later, I attended the Faculty of Law at Jan Kazimierz University, where I was privileged to study under the great Professor Oswald Balzer. One of the most brilliant students in my class, the Jew Raphael Lemkin, later became public prosecutor in Warsaw, but I gather that he fled when the Germans invaded Poland and is currently in the United States. Following my studies, I established myself as an attorney in Lwów [the Polish name of Lviv]. My mother and aunt remained on the estate in Mierzyn. I would like to emphasize that for many years the estate was managed by the Jew Szumer, a loyal and decent man, whose father had also served as our estate manager. Old Szumer retired shortly before the war and sold his house to the Hutsul, Dmytro Dowbusz, who also took over the management of the estate. The land in this region is very fertile, and thanks to its natural flora, it is also an excellent habitat for bees, and our estate was known for the outstanding honey produced in its numerous beehives. The flora also attracts an unusually large number of butterfly species. I returned to service as a captain in the Polish army in 1939 and was taken prisoner by the Germans in October. I managed to escape from the prisoner of war camp and traveled to the estate, where I found my older brother Władysław, whose medical practice in Warsaw had been destroyed in the German bombing of the city.

"In early February 1940, I cannot recall the precise date, at about 4 a.m., we awoke to the sound of loud banging on the main gate of the villa. Looking out of the second-floor window, I saw a group of uniformed men armed with rifles with fixed bayonets. When we opened the door, an NKVD official accompanied by a civilian with distinctly Jewish features ordered us to pack the necessary items for a long journey and be ready to leave within half an hour. When I inquired for the reason, he laughed out loud, slapped the little Jew on his back, and said, 'Mojsze here informs me that the whole lot of you are not only cursed nobles but also reactionary officers and have weapons stored in your house.' I now recognized the Jew as a wagon driver from Zakłócenie who would occasionally drive me from the train station to the center of the city when I arrived from Lwów to visit my mother. The officer ordered the soldiers to search the premises, while he and the Jew flopped down on the sofas in our sitting room, lit makhorka cigarettes, and instructed our maid to serve them vodka.

"My brother and I packed some clothes and were ready to leave within a few minutes. When the NKVD official saw us with our backpacks, he burst out laughing again, saying, 'You were too quick! I haven't even finished drinking!' Then he looked around and asked, 'Where is the old lady?' We tried to convince him that our mother was too frail to travel in winter, but he would have none of it, saying that they had brought a very comfortable sled especially for this purpose. Out of the corner of my eye, I could see the Jew Mojsze grinning. We helped our mother pack and took with us a down blanket to protect her on the way. By the time we left the villa, dawn was breaking, and I could see that some of the farmhands and villagers had gathered at a respectful distance from the soldiers. The NKVD officer was snickering. 'These muzhiks,' he said, 'they are just waiting for us to leave so they can loot the place.' As we climbed into the sled, the Jew Mojsze leaned over to me and whispered, 'I hope you survive.' But I could not tell whether this was meant sincerely or in derision. It took us several hours to reach the train station in Zakłócenie, where a long freight train was waiting. It was already quite full of civilians from the area. Our mother had fallen asleep, and we had tried to cover her as best we could, but when we arrived, we discovered that she was no longer alive. We did not know what to do with her body. A kind local Polish priest, a young man, who was there to comfort the deportees, promised to give her a proper burial. I have only recently heard that under the German occupation this Father Motyka moved to a nearby village where he hid several Jews.

"The train journey lasted about two weeks. There were more than 20 of us in the locked boxcar: several Polish officials and army veterans from Zakłócenie, two families with small children from a nearby Polish village, a Ukrainian couple with a nursing baby, two young Jewish women, one of whom was pregnant, and an older Jewish man who was apparently their father. By the time we arrived, the Ukrainian baby and one of the small Polish children had died, and the Jewish man was very sick with high fever and delirium. The boxcar was not heated, and we had very little to keep ourselves warm. We received only scraps of food when the train stopped and there was never enough water. We had only a bucket for our biological needs, and it could not be emptied when the train was moving. It was a hellish journey.

"We arrived at a settlement in Siberia, from which my brother and I, along with four other Polish veterans and former police officers, were sent to a labor camp. There we were employed cutting timber for close to a year and a half. Conditions were very harsh and many of the inmates succumbed to the cold, malnutrition, and illness. Among them was my brother Władysław, who died of typhus on June 20, 1941. A few days later we heard about the German invasion of the

Soviet Union, and later that summer those of us who were still relatively fit were released from the camp and transferred to a military barracks near Buzuluk in southwestern Russia, where Anders' Army was being built. Conditions there were also very harsh, and we suffered from disease and lack of food. But we were proud to be serving as Polish soldiers again. Thanks to my military background I was appointed captain and company commander despite my age. We trained daily and expected to be sent to the front to fight alongside the Red Army, the prospect of which we regarded with mixed feelings. But in spring 1942, we were transferred to the Caspian Sea and from there taken by ship to the Persian port of Bandar-e Pahlavi. A few weeks later we came under British command and were transferred to Palestine.

"During my time in Palestine, I took the opportunity to look up my two childhood friends, Jakób [Janek uses Yakov's Polish name] and Adolf Szumer, the sons of old Szumer, our former estate manager. I remembered that Adolf had gone to Palestine in the early 1930s; people said that things had gotten too hot for him as a communist activist. Jakób left a few years later with his wife and children as a Zionist. I thought it would be difficult to find them, but since I knew that they had initially settled in Petah Tikva, a small community not far from the city of Tel Aviv, all it took was for me to ask a few people on the street and they directed me to Jakób's home, a one-room shack in the back yard of a stone house. My intention was not merely to see these old friends after all that we had been through, but to inform them, to the best of my knowledge, of what had happened to the Jews of their town and in the region as a whole.

"While training in southwestern Russia, we were joined by a fair number of Polish Jews, quite a few of them from the areas of Eastern Poland occupied by the Germans in 1941. Some had left with the retreating Red Army forces, and others had managed to flee later on. Several of them were in communication with Jewish elements under German rule. We Poles also received information from the exiled

Polish government in London, including reports from the Home Army and other Polish agencies about the ongoing and accelerating slaughter of Jews. My assumption was that much of this information had not reached Palestine yet.

"When I walked into Jakób's modest but immaculately clean shack, neither he nor his wife were there. His daughter, who was taking care of her two younger brothers, told me in excellent Polish that they worked very hard and would not be back before dark. I left her the address of the hotel in Tel Aviv where we officers had been temporarily set up and asked her to tell her father that I would appreciate it if he could come, since we might be departing for Egypt at any time.

"That night, at about 9 p.m., both Jakób and Adolf came to my hotel. It had been a very hot day, as is common during that time of the year in Palestine, but the hotel was located close to the beach and an evening breeze made it quite comfortable. We sat down on the hotel's front porch, and I poured them some vodka from the bottle I had brought for the occasion. We toasted our reunion and I offered them pickled cucumbers and canned sardines from my army rations. British soldiers were walking along the beach, their arms wrapped around local Jewish girls. The radio in the hotel dining room was broadcasting the latest news from the fronts in North Africa and Russia. Both men looked older, and Adolf, the younger brother, seemed downcast. They told me about their families in Palestine, and I informed them of Władek's death, and our mother's passing, saying that I was now entirely alone in the world, not having had the good fortune of raising a family myself. We toasted all those we had lost. I could tell they were waiting for news from Poland, and I found it difficult to speak.

"Eventually I plucked up enough courage and told them everything I knew about the massacres of Jews by the Germans. There had been one mass killing in Zakłócenie in August 1941, shortly after the Wehrmacht marched in, in which several hundred Jews, apparently all men, the intellectual and professional elite of the community, were shot. More recently, there had been many other mass killings in nearby towns. We had not received any information about deportations from Zakłócenie yet, but it was probably just a matter of time. Jews were being deported to a camp near the village of Bełżec, not far from Rawa Ruska, where they were reportedly being killed instantaneously with electricity or gas. No one who had reached that camp managed to escape. We also knew that the Germans had established formations of Ukrainian auxiliary police, which were assisting them in these massacres. When we return to our lands and homes, we will avenge the innocent victims, I vowed.

"We sat up much of the night, drinking and reminiscing about our carefree childhood in Mierzyn. We recalled our soccer games with the village youth; Ukrainians, Poles, and Jews playing together, as if no social or religious barriers existed between us. On Fridays, old Szumer's wife would bake sweet bread and their sister Rachela [Rochaleh's Polish name] would always bring us a few slices. I remembered watching the boys and their father standing by the little stream flowing to the Dniester, fervently praying on their holiest day, their Day of Atonement, and emptying their pockets to symbolically repent their sins. On the Feast of Tabernacles, they would build a little hut with a thatched roof and have their meals there, always singing together, and if it rained or snowed only old Szumer would take his meals there. Our mother did not allow the boys into our villa, but they would sneak into the grounds and we'd play hide and seek.

"I looked across the promenade, where very few people could be seen now, and out to the sea, its dark, warm waves lapping against the dunes. The air was heavy with moisture, and I thought to myself how far we had come from that world of our childhood, where our ancestors had lived side-by-side for so many centuries. Deep in my heart I knew that we would never come back there, that it was all over and could never be repaired. In truth, apart from that shared childhood in our little village, where the bees made the sweetest honey I have ever tasted, and the butterflies were more varied and beautiful than in any other place on this earth, beyond that morsel of dirt on which we all grew up, we had nothing in common, these two rough, heavyset Jews in Palestine and myself, scion of one of the oldest noble families in Poland, but for the fact that we had lost everything we had and would never be able to make it good again.

"A few days later, we were transferred to Egypt and trained there with British forces. In February 1944, as part of the II Polish Corps, we shipped off to Italy and in May participated in the Fourth Battle of Monte Cassino, where our brave Polish fighters contributed mightily to the capture of the abbey despite very heavy casualties. I will never forget the moment when the Polish flag was hoisted next to the Union Jack over the ruins of the monastery on May 18. We fought in Italy well into 1945, and another memory that will always remain with me is our encounter with troops from the Jewish Brigade, which was also part of the British Eighth Army in Italy. They had fought bravely along the Senio River in March 1945, and the following month, as our forces were preparing to launch an offensive on Bologna, I proposed that we arrange an evening together with those men from Palestine who were camped nearby.

"Many of us Poles had come from parts of Poland where there had been many Jews, and not a few of my men had hostile attitudes toward the Jews of their communities before the war, and spoke of them as having collaborated with the Soviets and facilitated their deportation. We were pleasantly surprised to encounter these young, athletic men from Palestine, at least as eager as we were to fight the Germans who had destroyed their families just as they had destroyed our own.

"I was especially intrigued by one young man, certainly not older than 18, who spoke with me about the dilemma of revenge. 'We,' he said, 'want to avenge our murdered families by killing and destroying, yes, even wiping out the entire German people, raping their women, and slaughtering their children, so that the world remembers never to do to us again what the Germans have done.' His black eyes were burning with rage as he spoke, and for a moment he appeared to me like God's avenging angel with his flaming sword. 'But then,' the young man continued, his expression softening, 'then we know that if we were to act in this manner, we would be no better than our enemies and the murderers of our people. And we, as Zionists, want to build for ourselves a new country, a just society, and one cannot do that only with hatred in one's heart and the blood of innocents on one's hands. But then again, if we do not fight like devils, mercilessly and brutally, then all the old accusations about us Jews will resurface; that we are the cowardly and effeminate sons of a subjugated people that has lost all its warlike qualities over millennia of exile. This is our dilemma,' he said.

"'You know,' I said to him, 'I grew up with two young Jewish men in my village, and they were anything but cowardly or effeminate. They were big, strong men who could beat any of the Ukrainian village boys and feared no one.'

"'And where are they now?' he asked.

"'In Palestine,' I said, 'I met them there a couple of years ago.'

"'Where did they come from?'

"'They grew up with me in Mierzyn, but later on moved to Zakłócenie, which you Jews call Zaklots, and emigrated to Palestine before the war.'

"'Are they called Yakov and Adolf? Yakov's daughter is my girlfriend,' he said with astonishment. 'If we ever get out of this war alive and I make it back to Palestine, I hope to marry her.'

"He suddenly looked like the young, tender boy that he was, and not that fierce, bloodthirsty avenger he had pretended to be, or perhaps simultaneously embodied. I felt as if an entire cycle of my own life had come to an end. Whatever happens to me in the future exile to which I seem doomed, I will always remember this as a moment of triumph, a sign that life will always reassert itself even following the greatest tragedy and devastation.

"In conclusion, I would like to say for the record, because I know the sentiments currently reigning among Poles, that the Jews I knew in my village and the Jews with whom I fought were decent brave folk and did not deserve hatred and mass murder."

IZI

This was how I learned that as a young soldier in the Jewish Brigade, my father had met Janek, then a British Army captain in the II Polish Corps in Italy, the only surviving son of the Grafina of Mierzyn, the village where my grandfather and my mother were born. Reading this account, I realized that it was time for me to return to Israel and sort out my father's papers, as his widow had long been urging me to do. Additionally, the first anniversary of his death was coming up, conveniently just after the end of the fall semester. And so, in December 2017 I went back to Israel for two weeks.

The apartment had not changed much. Over the decades, since I had left first to do my army service in the early 1970s, followed by university studies in Britain and finally a move to North America, it had seen a few changes, but far fewer than those experienced by its inhabitants. Now they were all gone, save for my father's widow, who had moved in only a few years before his death. What had once been my teenage bedroom was now her study, but my father's study was still as he had left it, and it was there that I spent a fair amount of time, going through old papers, articles, books, photo albums and drafts. His laptop, a growing source of frustration in his old age, was filled with files and folders that needed some organization. He had reigned supreme as a master of the typewriter, typing at breakneck speed, pulling out papers with one stroke, rapidly crumpling them into balls, throwing them into the wastepaper basket across the room, missing it as often as scoring, all with an eternal cigarette hanging from the corner of his mouth and the room filled with a cloud of smoke that tilted this way and that as the machine's little bell announced the end of a line and a quick jerk of the lever moved it to the next. The transition to a computer had slowed him down with its endless idiosyncrasies and snares, swallowing documents and refusing to divulge them, requiring ever more passwords that could not be remembered, and gradually transforming the writing process into an endless loop of copies of copies of copies, each of them similar to the last but never quite the same, assuming an identity of its own that their author could never entirely control, until an obliging grandson would show up, and with a couple of clicks return things to normal for another day.

The books on the shelves were in double rows for lack of space. While trying to select which to keep and which to discard, one volume attracted my attention. On the white cover of this hardbound book, spotted gray with age, there were only two Hebrew words in black letters, *Sefer Vosok*, the Vosok Memorial Book. I faintly recalled having seen this volume before. Vosok, I remembered from my mother's account, was the little Carpathian town where two of her uncles and their families were murdered. Why had they moved there from their ancestral village on the banks of the Czeremosz before the war? Were they transferred there by the Germans to facilitate their murder? I knew practically nothing about them, but for the fact that one of them, Chaim, was a violinist.

I sat down on my father's sofa, where he used to take afternoon naps, and leafed through the pages. I could find no mention of the Berman family. After all, they must have only lived there for a short time. A batch of thin, neatly folded papers had been inserted close to the back of the book, marking a long list of names under the heading, 'The holy and the pure, murdered by the Nazis and their helpers.' It was there that I found, underlined in blue pen, the names 'Berman Chaim, his wife Raisel, and their two children,' and 'Berman Ovadia and his wife Raisel.' My grandfather, who had spent his last years looking through the collection of memorial books he had accumulated from his and other Galician towns, must have marked these names of his wife's brothers and their families. I carefully unfolded the sheets of paper, which were covered by an undated, densely written, but quite legible Yiddish text addressed to my grandfather and signed 'Your cousin, Izi Szumer.' Izi, I remembered from my mother's letter, was the only member of the family to have emerged unscathed from the slaughter, the man my grandfather had shunned as a Nazi collaborator. The following is my translation.

"Before I put an end to my wretched life and vanish forever from this cursed earth, I wish to describe some of the events that I experienced under the rule of the wicked occupiers, events of which there is no other record but my own recollections. I write this not to justify my actions or to seek forgiveness, but to inform you of the cruel fates of the Berman family and of all the other Jews of Vosok, so that you understand the horrible circumstances in which the Jews found themselves during those times. You may want to discard these pages or destroy them altogether, as you may wish to do with me, but at least I will know that you had the opportunity to read them and to reflect upon their meaning.

"As you know, I grew up in a small village close to Vosok, where my father, who was not as successful as his older brother, your respected father, made his living as a tavern keeper. He worked hard all his life, as did my mother, and I need not remind you that these were not easy times that became even harder in the years after you and your family

116

went to Palestine. The tavern was a source of income, but was also a cesspool of bitterness, dissolution, and rage. Every week the peasants would either drink themselves under the table or curse and threaten my father for refusing to give them any more credit, or for diluting the vodka, or for making them addicted to alcohol and swiping the last penny from them.

"I hated my life in that filthy little village, growing up surrounded by dirty urchins who were constantly on the prowl for food or mischief in their tattered clothes and bare feet. I grew up to be a not too bad-looking lad and was glad when my father sent me to the cheder and then to the public school in Vosok to get the education he never had, so that I would make something of myself as his only child and heir. I liked reading, especially fiction, and loved Berdyczewski and Peretz and Feierbeg, whom I read in Yiddish and Hebrew, and also Franzos, the first novelist I ever read in German. I know that you grew up on your father's farm and cherished nature and physical work, but I liked reading about the exploits of others, even though, like all Szumers, I was blessed with a robust physique. I was not a very good student and preferred keeping the company of young women and dressing as well as I could afford on the meagre allowance from my father.

"You may have heard about my two failed marriages to Fayge and Leah. Fayge came from a good home in Vosok and was a beautiful but very fragile young woman. Her parents feared that she would never marry because of her permanent ill health and took a liking to me because of my good manners and looks. My father's business was still doing relatively well at the time, whereas they had had to marry off three daughters, Fayge being the oldest. We had a good couple of years together in Vosok, and I helped in her father's clothing store, where the female clients in particular took a liking to me. Then Fayge died in childbirth, along with the baby, and I was left on my own. There is no reason to spend time here on my second marriage to

Leah, apart from to say that she gave me neither children nor happiness. Being the spoilt daughter of one of the richest men in Vosok, much as I always liked beautiful women, she was unable to resist handsome men, and by the time we divorced I had entirely abandoned any hope of love and happiness, returned to my aging parents, and cut myself off from all worldly affairs.

"I spent my time reading books and newspapers most of the day, going for long walks in the forests, and dreaming of the life I knew I could no longer have; somewhere in a big, cosmopolitan city, where people would be elegantly dressed and well spoken, where cafés would be clean and filled with intelligent conversation, and I would be engaged in something interesting and perhaps even useful such as writing for a newspaper or advising well-read clients on the latest novel in my own bookstore. By then, you may recall, I had come to be known as the *chudak*, the oddball of the family. I rarely attended family gatherings, knowing that everyone saw me as a failure, even if in my heart of hearts, I knew that if only I tried hard enough, I could do better than any of them, yet I no longer wanted to. But I was not a bad person.

"When the Russians came in 1939, they immediately nationalized my father's tavern but kept him on as manager. Things did not change that much at the beginning, apart from the fact that there was now less food, the alcohol supplied to us was of poor quality, and the newspapers became extremely boring, all of them running almost precisely the same items. We all had to vote, and because there was only one candidate the Soviets won a landslide victory and we became part of Soviet Ukraine. Then the deportations began. There were a few Polish estate owners in the region, and some former government and police officials in Vosok, and they were almost all rounded up, packed into a train, and sent far into the interior of the Soviet Union. I don't know if any of them ever came back.

"Among them was a young woman, Elżbieta, whom I dearly loved, although we could meet only in the forest, because her father had been a high-ranking Polish official and an Endek—a follower of that antisemitic party that wanted us all to go to Palestine before the war —and my father, as you may know, however kind and tolerant he had always been with me, would have had none of me going with a Christian woman. The poor girl, who was a good 10 years younger than me, was taken, and I pray that she survived. Perhaps God did not want her to see what later became of me. Why did we not go to Palestine as you and Adolf did when there was still time? I think my father could not stomach the idea of starting a new life. All he had was the tavern. What would he have done in Palestine? As for me, it was just inertia. I thought I would be equally comfortable, or uncomfortable, wherever I was, so there was no reason to move. In my imagination I could always fantasize about the life I might still have. I could have never imagined what was about to happen.

"There were also deportations of Jews, and I recall some of my most outspoken Zionist friends being rounded up or going into hiding. But Father had nothing to worry about, because the Russians like alcohol as much as the next man, or actually much more. And I pretended to be his assistant, though I rarely did much to help. Then the local militia, which included Jews from the city and surrounding towns, began arresting Ukrainians, some who had been nationalist activists before the war and antisemitic to boot, and others who were decent folk. They took young hotheads and older promoters of education and readings clubs, and soon everyone grew scared of a knock on the door in the middle of the night. Whenever I went to town I would suffer dark looks from the locals, as if I had anything to do with the arrest of their family members and friends simply because I was a Jew. Prisoners were beaten up and tortured in the local jail, and the militia would park a big truck in front of the police station and run its engine to cover the screams of the victims. An old classmate joined the militia, but I won't mention his name. He later fled with the Soviets, and his family was slaughtered by the locals.

"The day the Russians pulled out my father was murdered. Some villagers broke into the tavern and ransacked it. Like all of us Szumers, my father was a big, strong man, even though he was no longer young. He picked up a club he kept behind the counter and faced his attackers. They overpowered him and beat him so hard that he lost consciousness. Then they hanged him from a beam in our house. My mother screamed until she lost her voice. She never spoke again, would not eat, and died within a few months. I was in Vosok that day and by the time I got back to our village it was all over. My friend, Hryn, who had watched from a distance, told me what had happened. Whether he had participated in the looting I could not tell.

"There was no point staying in the house, and in any case our lives were in danger in the village, so we moved to Vosok. By the time we arrived, the town had been taken over by the Ukrainian militia, and a blue-and-yellow flag was flying from the roof of the city hall. Some drunken peasants had converged on the town from nearby villages and were breaking into Jewish homes. My mother and I found shelter with Fayge's elderly parents. They were glad to have a young, strong man move in with them at this time of chaos. Their other daughters had married and moved to other towns, so there was sufficient room for us. We sealed all the windows with wooden shutters and blocked the door, then we sat in the dark and waited for the Germans. We were sure that they would reinstate order. We remembered how in the last war the German and Austrian troops had been far better behaved than the Russians, especially to us Jews.

"The Germans arrived a couple of days later and after a few weeks of terror finally put an end to the mayhem. First, they appointed a Jewish Council, made up of the notables from the town, and in turn ordered it to appoint a Jewish police force. We were told that the members of the Jewish police and their families would be protected from any measures imposed by the authorities and receive better food. It was clear to me that by being a policeman I could better take care of my mother and Fayge's parents. Altogether there were about 20 of us, and I was soon made chief because I was older and taller than most of the others and could speak both Ukrainian and German.

"That summer, our main job was to collect money and various items demanded by the Germans. There were not many Germans in the town, just a few administrators and a small police force of mostly middle-aged gendarmes. We got along with them quite well. Our relations with the Ukrainian police force the Germans had created were less friendly, because many of them had been militant nationalists before the war, and some had taken part in pogroms after the Soviets withdrew. Unlike us, they were armed with rifles and were always looking for trouble, whether drunk or sober. I will admit that during the requisitions from the richer Jews in the town we were not always very gentle, and that we pilfered some items for ourselves. Soon we were dressed well, wearing elegant shirts and pants and fine boots, and later also well-made coats. We could not afford to take no for an answer from any Jew, because then we would be punished by the Germans. Those who resisted were slapped around a bit and if they persisted were taken to the Jewish Council, where they would be detained or handed over to the Ukrainians or the Germans. Few people were stupid enough to stand in our way. Only the working-class Jewish lads gave us a hard time. Sometimes we got into fists fights with them and chased them around town, to the Germans' and Ukrainians' merriment.

"After a few weeks an order went out from the Jewish Council to be ready for a special operation before dawn. We assembled in our meeting room, a synagogue adjacent to the Jewish Council's offices, which were located in the former Tarbut Hebrew school. We were armed with batons and had white armbands with the letters OD in blue on them, denoting *Ordnungsdienst* or order service. The local Ukrainian police milled about on the street. At about 5 a.m., a large black car arrived with German police officials we had not seen before, followed by a truck with heavily armed Ukrainian auxiliary police personnel. The German officials went into the Jewish Council's office, and then we OD men were ordered to go from door to door and announce that all Jewish men aged 16 to 60 were to assemble at the market square by 6 a.m. As the Jews scrambled out of their beds and headed toward the square, the local Ukrainian police rushed them along with kicks and rifle butts, while the auxiliary police surrounded the square to make sure no one could escape.

"The men stood in the square as the sun gradually rose over the nearby hill, trembling in the morning chill, while the German officials finished the breakfast laid for them by the Jewish Council. The Germans, all dressed in elegant black uniforms, shiny boots, tall caps, and armed with pistols and submachine guns, then walked over to the square. The order was to sort out members of white-collar professions from working men. The latter were allowed to return to their homes, and the doctors and dentists were also sent away. The remaining 200 or so men were marched out of town toward the Jewish cemetery on the slopes of the hill. We had heard from larger towns what the Germans did to members of the Jewish intelligentsia, and everyone was very fearful.

"As we neared the cemetery, a few Jewish men tried to dash off into the woods. They were instantaneously shot by the Ukrainians and Germans. One of them was Ovadia Berman, your dear wife's brother, who had worked in the Tarbut school as a teacher before the war. As I walked past him, I could clearly identify his features. In some ways he was fortunate to have been spared all that came after, but I felt sorry for his wife Raisel, who was now left to fend for herself, as they had no children. They were still quite young.

"The Jews were then handed tools by the local police and told to dig a trench. It was getting hot, and they removed their coats clothing as they worked. Many had never done any physical labor and were mocked and abused by the Ukrainians. It turned into a beautiful summer day. There were birds everywhere, the insects were buzzing, and the flowers were in bloom. We could hear the wailing of the women in the town. By noon the trench was ready. The men were ordered to take off all their clothes and stand on the edge in groups of ten. Then the German officials shot them with short bursts from their submachine guns. At least this is how I remember it; later they would shoot the Jews with a single pistol or rifle shot in the back of the neck. It did not take long to kill the entire group. A table had been set next to the site with sandwiches and several bottles of vodka, all supplied by the Jewish Council, so that the German officials could celebrate their achievement. The OD was ordered to cover up the pit. Some men were not yet dead and writhing in pain, but the Germans saw no reason to waste any more bullets on them and walked off. They were followed by the auxiliary policemen, many of whom grabbed the choicest items of clothing left behind by the victims.

"After this roundup there was a lull in the killing that lasted about a year, during which we hardly ever saw the German police officials who had killed our fellow Jews. The event we had witnessed had greatly demoralized the OD men and I sought ways to cheer them. During one of our patrols in the city I encountered Chaim Berman, your dear wife's other brother. He looked quite wretched. Before the Germans, he had made a decent living as a violinist, playing with a few other musicians at weddings, bar mitzvahs, and other celebrations, not only for Jews. He had trained as a classical violinist but after the war began, he could no longer work with real orchestras. Now, under German rule, there was nothing to celebrate and

Chaim's family, his wife Raisel and his two children, were starving. I suggested that he come to our headquarters in the former synagogue and perform for us, not the usual klezmer fare but real classical works, and we would compensate him handsomely with food, clothes, and some money. In this manner Chaim became our court musician, as we called him.

"Once he began playing for us, the Jewish Council started showing an interest in his abilities and arranged several performances for their own officials and their families. Soon Chaim's reputation as a classical violinist also reached the local German administration. From a wretchedly poor and hungry little fiddler Chaim became a celebrity, and even the German administrators, who appreciated, or pretended to appreciate, classical music, would compensate him for his moving performances with various items, most of which they had previously stolen from the Jews.

"Chaim was not the only Jew who became popular with the Germans. The Landkommissar, Herr Hoffmann, who oversaw the economic development of the town and region of Vosok, employed several young Jewish women as translators and typists. Other women worked in German homes, cleaning, cooking, and shopping. Jewish doctors, especially dentists, were very popular, performing their services free of charge, since no one would dare ask a German official for a fee. For several months, the somber mood that had taken over the Jews of Vosok lifted, and even we OD men began to forget the tragic episode we had been forced to witness.

"All this changed the following year. My beloved cousin Yakov, I cannot describe all the horrors that occurred and how deeply mired the OD became in the slaughter of our own community. We did what we could for our fellow Jews. But we also wanted to protect our loved ones, and we followed the injunctions of the Jewish Council, whose leaders, the most respected members of the community, repeatedly told us that we had to preserve the best elements even at the price of letting go of lesser ones, the dust of humanity that exists in every community and becomes all the more visible at times of crisis. I should say that there were those within the Jewish Council itself who did not conduct themselves in a manner that did honor to the Jewish people.

"There were altogether five roundups between October 1942 and June 1943. We were charged with breaking down the doors of Jewish homes using axes and crowbars, and then dragging the inhabitants out of their homes, to be marched off to assembly points under the guard of the Ukrainians. We were also charged with looking for hiding places; underground bunkers, hidden attics, ingeniously built shelters under staircases and floors. The Germans did not dare crawl into these dark and smelly spaces and ordered us to do so. On one such occasion I crawled into a bunker and found Chaim's wife Raisel and their two children hiding there with several other families. I forced all the other Jews to come out but left Raisel and her children there, telling the Germans that everyone was out. Just as we were about to leave the sound of a weeping child came from inside the bunker. The Gestapo official in charge slapped me hard across the face and screamed, 'You filthy Jew, crawl back in there and get them all out!' By the time I reached them, all three were dead. Chaim later told me that he had procured poison from our pharmacist for a steep price and given it to Raisel to use if they were caught. He did not want them to suffer the horror of the killing pits.

"Following this event, I was demoted from my position as chief of the OD but was kept on the force. Others were trying to join us, believing that this was the only way to survive. We had grown to 30 men as the killings increased in frequency and ferocity. In the aftermath of each roundup, the streets would be strewn with bodies; babies that had been thrown out of second-floor windows would be lying in the gutters with spattered brains. During one of these roundups it was snowing heavily, and for days thereafter the snow was stained red with blood.

"We no longer knew what we were doing and staggered from one house to another, pulling people out, beating, cursing, weeping. We were no longer human beings but beasts of prey, or worse, demons doing Satan's work. We kept Chaim with us and when we returned to our quarters, where we now slept for fear of being caught in a roundup and killed ourselves, he would play sweet melodies for us, and our hearts would melt for a few moments before we dropped into a death-like sleep filled with terror and fear. Chaim had changed beyond recognition after the death of his family. He hardly ate, though we always had plenty of food, and he hardly slept. He just sat in his corner, his violin on his lap, his eyes glowing strangely like coals in a dying fire.

"Finally, as we had expected, the Germans and Ukrainians came for us. This was in June 1943 and as we had heard, the German police had been ordered to make all of Galicia Jew-free. We had prepared ourselves for this. We had a couple of stolen pistols and a sawed-off shotgun, a few hand grenades, and several axes. When the Ukrainian police first approached our building, we scared them off. We celebrated our victory with a bottle of vodka. Then we noticed that Chaim was no longer there. When the Ukrainians returned, this time accompanied by German gendarmes, they surrounded us from all sides. As the shooting began, we could hear Chaim playing his violin, but could not tell where he was. He was no longer playing classical music, Mozart, Beethoven, Bach, but Jewish music, merry and melancholy klezmer tunes, as if we were at a wedding, a bar mitzvah, a circumcision. As he played, we were subjected to a hail of bullets and fell one by one. In a last desperate effort, the handful of us who survived set fire to the synagogue, hurled our hand grenades at the Ukrainians guarding the back entrance, and in the confusion that ensued made a dash for the forest. I was the only one to reach the first line of trees. When I looked back, I saw my comrades on the ground, some still alive and trying to crawl toward the forest. The synagogue was now engulfed in flames, but on its roof I could see a human figure through the smoke. A few last notes came from his violin, and then the whole edifice disintegrated and came crashing down.

"In the forest I joined a small Jewish resistance group. Later we became part of a partisan formation. I will not bother you with all the battles, killings, and deaths I experienced. I was awarded a Soviet medal for bravery. I killed many Ukrainians and Germans. When I came to Palestine, as you may know, I joined the Jewish forces in 1948 and killed many Arabs. I was not known for being merciful and I think my comrades learned to fear me. I never tried to associate with the few survivors from Vosok who ended up in Israel. When I came to you, I was not looking for mercy or understanding or even compassion. I was just very lonely and hoped, stupidly as I now know, to have a family, even if only on the holidays. Recently, someone recognized me on the street in Tel Aviv. 'Kapo!' he shouted, 'he was a Kapo, worse than the Germans!' People stared at me, not knowing what to do. No one dared approach me, so I just walked on. I will stop here. Perhaps you will read this and perhaps one of your children or the grandchildren you may be blessed with will find this one day. May they make of this letter what they will. Your loving cousin, Izi."

MYKHAILO

I did not share Izi's letter with anyone. I put it back in the memorial book and took the book, along with several other items from my father's study, with me to North America. I thought of scanning and sending the letter to Tali, but I was not sure she could read Yiddish and did not then have time to translate it. I was also unclear about where she was. Had she returned to Israel or stayed in New Zealand? It did not really matter, since I had her email address, but somehow I thought that it would make a difference. I did not hear from her for a long time. It appeared that things had been more or less resolved. I certainly knew much more about what had happened to members of my family during the war, and Tali also had at least a version of the events that led to the death of her mother's best and only childhood friend. But of course there was no closure, nor could there ever be.

In April 2019, I finally received an email from Tali. I had written to her a few times, but she had not responded. I thought that perhaps she regretted having confided in me, considering that we hardly knew each other, and decided to put an end to our exchange. Perhaps that trip to New Zealand had triggered in her a desire to start a new life, free from the weight of her own past and her family's history.

"I apologize for my silence," she wrote. "There was much that I needed to figure out for myself, and it took time to process everything. I should let you know that I decided to stay in New Zealand. I was appointed permanent director of our office in Wellington and am very happy about that. As I wrote to you in the past, I like this country both for what it is and for what it is not. It is the kind of place where I can start a new chapter in my life. And I am doing just that. I met someone here and we will be moving in together in the next few months. He is an Italian, not a Kiwi, but has been teaching art and film here at the university for quite a few years. He is older than I am, closer to your age, and will retire soon. Massimo is very good to me. He is gentle, warm, smart, and funny. He cooks well and loves beautiful things. He is divorced with two children, who are already grown and independent. I can imagine living with him for the rest of my life. We may go to visit his family in Italy in the summer (our winter break). I have not been to Italy for a while and am looking forward to it.

"But this is not the reason I decided to write to you. As you may recall, when we last communicated, I mentioned that I had put the whole story with Andriy behind me, but that I might still check on him. It took some time, but eventually I wrote to ask him how he was doing. He responded almost instantaneously. He was in a rather dark mood, and was glad to hear from me, because although I was very far, we had known each other quite intimately, even if only for a couple of weeks, and over the past few months he had been thinking a great deal about that time we had together. He now has a permanent position at the University of Leicester, or at least as permanent as academic positions can be in the UK these days. He has published a revised version of his thesis, which focused on the spread of Ukrainian nationalism among peasants in Galicia. His new research concerns Russian and Soviet nationality politics in Ukraine.

"In his personal life he has faced some challenges. He was in a long-term relationship with a woman from Leicester, whom he met at an academic conference. In fact, she was one reason behind his decision to apply for the job there, and initially they were very happy to be able to move in together. But he could not quite make up his mind about marrying her, and although she was a little younger, she felt that her chances of having children were slipping away, whereas he was not ready to have a family.

"Five years ago, Andriy's mother died within months of being diagnosed with pancreatic cancer. 'For some reason,' he wrote, 'her death made me realize that our lives together were going nowhere. Perhaps it was because the intense heartbreak that I experienced exposed the shallowness of a relationship that had become largely a matter of comfort and convenience. Perhaps it was because I suddenly missed everything about my mother that had embarrassed me in my youth; her accent, foreign manners, the few hints of her Jewish identity, everything that the woman I was living with was not. What had initially attracted me to her, now made her seem impossibly far from all that truly mattered to me. But maybe I was just looking for excuses to break it off due to my fear of commitment and my sense that I simply was not ready, and likely would never be ready, to raise a family. In any case, this conventional midlife crisis is not what I wanted to tell you about.

"'What is more to the point is that last year my grandfather passed away. He was well into his nineties, so that hardly came as a shock. I could not attend the funeral because I was on a research trip to Russia and returned to the UK only a couple of months later. During a visit to my father in Gloucester, he showed me a box that Grandfather had instructed him to give me. My father, by the way, is in bad shape. He could not get over the loss of my mother, sold his auto shop, and hardly leaves the house. In any case, inside the box was a notebook written in Ukrainian. My father had never really learned to read the language, although he spoke it with Grandfather, but he must have been able to make out the two words written on the cover of the notebook: "My confession." I don't know if he was tempted to try and read it, but as he told me, Grandfather had explicitly said that the box was to be given to me, and only to me.'

"Andriy spent the next few weeks transcribing this handwritten document and then translating it into English. He did not say whether he showed it to his father, and my sense is that he did not know what to do with it. When he heard from me, he asked whether he could share this confession with me. I have read it and have attached it to this email. I do not quite know what to say. It is simply devastating. Perhaps it is also true. In any case, it tells a different story about what happened in Mierzyn. Andriy wrote to me that he would have to live with that truth for the rest of his life, and at the same time accept that he might never know the whole truth. What he does know is that his grandfather, whom he loved very much, lied to him all those years. He said that he does not want to deal with this matter any longer, because he fears that its shadow will overwhelm him and make it impossible for him to move forward. And yet, there is a reference to another document in that confession. It is a Jewish document, and he is unfamiliar with either the relevant languages or archival collections. If by any chance I could find it, or knew someone who might be able to help, he would be grateful.

"I feel somewhat like Andriy. I am happy here where I am. I have a good job, I live in a beautiful city, and I have a lovely partner. He may not be as handsome as Andriy or as smart as you, but he loves me in an open, sincere, uncomplicated way. He is good for me. I cannot afford, psychologically, to keep getting pulled back to those sites and scenes that destroyed my family and drove my grandmother to suicide and my mother to insanity. Perhaps their condition was congenital, in which case I may not be able to escape it either. Be that as it may, I think I know as much as I want to know. But if by any chance you find the document Mykhailo mentions at the end of his confession, please do let me know. I will sign off here. I do hope you too find your happiness and your place in the world. It is never too late."

132

I saved the attachment to my laptop and decided not to read it right away. Only on Sunday, after sleeping in at the end of a busy week, did I finally settle down with Mykhailo's confession. I cannot say how closely Andriy's translation adhered to the original text, which I have not seen. My sense is that he might have elaborated it a little, possibly in an attempt to make Mykhailo appear more complex and sympathetic. Perhaps I am being unfair. In any case, I have not made any changes to this text.

"I am leaving this confession to my dear grandson Andriy. Andriy is a fine young man, a good son and grandson, a loyal citizen of this country, and a proud Ukrainian. He has studied our language and is a scholar with a degree from Oxford, the very first doctor in the Konovalets clan's long history. We are a family of peasants. My great-grandfather was born a serf, as were his ancestors for many generations. Even after we were emancipated, the Polish landowners and their Jewish lackeys bossed us about.

"I was born on a small farm that could not sustain my family. My father sent me to work as a stableboy on the Grafina's estate in Myryn when I was 13, and I remained there until 1944, when I decided to join the Ukrainian Insurgent Army at the age of 20. The estate manager was the Jew Szumer, who had been there for as long as anyone could remember and was said to have inherited this position from his father. Shortly before the war, old Szumer retired and the Hutsul Dmytro took over as estate manager.

"That summer, Szumer's daughter, her husband, and their little daughter visited the estate, together with another young woman and her little girl. I remember this visit very well because I was told by Dmytro to accompany them to the Grafina's villa. They were speaking with each other in a language I could not understand but which Dmytro later told me was Yiddish, the language of the Jews. The other woman spoke another language with her girl, which none of us recognized. It was a hot summer day and there were butterflies everywhere. The estate was famous for its butterflies, which were attracted to the flowers, and for its very good honey, produced in our many beehives. The sons of the Grafina were visiting as well that summer. I recall that they spoke with the young women in Polish, a language I had learned in the village school where we had a Polish teacher, even though the parents protested that they wanted their children to study in Ukrainian.

"My dearest grandson Andriy, I am telling you about this visit because of what happened later. It is that event that has made me sit down and write this confession. I know that I will die soon, and I cannot take this secret, which I have kept for so long, to the grave with me. I do not know what you will do with what I am about to tell you, and for me it will be too late. But I feel that you should know. I ought to have told your father. But he and I were never close. Perhaps he always sensed that I did not tell him the whole truth about the war, but then he never wanted to know about it. He wanted to be an Englishman and got impatient when it came to stories about the old country. You were always curious and have learned more about it than I will ever know, even though you were born in this country. This is why I am leaving this confession with you. You may do with it as you wish.

"Work on the estate was very hard, and I was always wretchedly poor. I preferred living on the estate, instead of walking back to the farm each day, even though the living quarters for us laborers were quite primitive. My family home was very crowded, and my father would often get drunk and beat us with a stick. Once we were grown, he no longer dared to beat us, and we sometimes protected our mother from him, because he would beat her too.

"On the estate I was left in peace, and I got along with Dmytro, although he spoke a strange dialect. I also made friends with some young men in the village who had more education than me and were reading newspapers and all kinds of pamphlets. It was from them that I heard about the Organization of Ukrainian Nationalists, which was illegal at the time, and how it was fighting to liberate us from the Polish lords and the Jewish parasites. The Polish authorities could have severely punished me for belonging to the OUN, but the organization gave a new meaning to my life, which otherwise consisted of working at least 12 hours a day, and then going to church on Sunday morning and drinking for the rest of the day to dull the sense of hopelessness.

"We would all converge on Yankel's little tavern at the edge of the village, drink as much as we could afford, curse him for not giving us more when we ran out of money, and sleep it off wherever out feet would carry us. Sometimes we would pass out right there in the tavern, only to wake up and begin another week of toil and sweat. Yankel was shot by someone in 1939 just after the Poles had fled from the region but before the Russians marched in, I think by one of ours, but no one ever admitted it. The Soviets made his tavern into a state store and vodka was soon hard to come by and increasingly expensive on the black market. But by then I was less interested in drinking. The head of our OUN cell berated me for getting drunk every Sunday, saying no proud Ukrainian should drink, certainly not lads my age, and that we were drinking away Ukraine's future and enriching the blood-sucking Jews. Instead, we should prepare for the battle for independence that would surely come, when we would purge ourselves of the Poles and the Jews and build a free and prosperous future.

"Stepan's lectures on Sunday afternoons replaced the drinking even before the Russians came, and then under the Soviets we kept on meeting, though it was much more dangerous. We were always afraid that the NKVD was on our trail or that one of our own would turn out to be a mole. We declared ourselves to be followers of Bandera, the young leader of the organization's radical faction whom we all admired, and we made elaborate plans for the day of insurrection against our oppressors. But in June 1941, the NKVD arrested Stepan and several other members of the cell and took them away from the village. We later heard that they were executed by the Soviets as soon as the Germans invaded later that month. The NKVD might well have arrested me too, but either they didn't have time or thought I was small fry and not worth the trouble. Still, I lived in terrible fear until the Germans arrived and I knew that the butchers of the NKVD could not reach me.

"Life under the Germans was not that different, but I no longer had Stepan and the others to give it meaning. At first, the Germans were friendly with us, then they began insisting on more and more contributions from the peasants for their army and their own people in Germany, even if it meant that we would starve. Some of our young men and women volunteered to work in Germany, where they were promised good wages and better food. Then we heard that the English and American were bombing Germany and people no longer wanted to go there. Still the Germans needed to send more and more men to fight against the Russians, and someone had to do the work in their fields and factories at home, so they would go on raids in our villages and snatch anyone they could find and send them to Germany. I was not so worried about this because Dmytro, who was now the only boss of the estate after the Poles had been deported by the Soviets, was an efficient manager and complied with all the

German demands for supplies in return for being allowed keep his workers.

"We heard terrible stories about what was happening to the Jews in the towns and cities, although we saw none of it because there were no Jews in our village. We felt sorry for all those poor people who, as we heard, were led to their graves and shot—men, women, old people, and children. We could not understand why they did not resist and fight back, after all, at least they would have died fighting, not like sheep led to the slaughter. Some of us said that this was perhaps preordained by God, that they were paying for what they did to Jesus and accepted it as divine justice. I did not really believe any of this. Others said that what was happening to the Jews was terrible but at least we would finally be rid of them, and after the war was over, would have Ukraine all to ourselves if we could only get rid of the Poles. And still others said that the Jews were getting what they deserved, that they were guilty of killing our patriots, like Stepan, because they collaborated with the Soviets, and that in any case, all the Bolsheviks were Jews. I cannot vouch for that because, as I said, there were no Jews in our village after old Szumer left, and poor Yankel was killed. I am quite sure that neither of them was a Bolshevik.

"Dmytro lived in a big farmhouse not far from the Grafina's villa. I heard that she died shortly after the Soviets arrested her and her sons. No one moved into their house, although our people largely emptied it of its contents. Throughout the war you could see some of our village girls wearing fancy but ill-fitting clothes that their suitors had stolen from the villa and given them as presents. We laborers lived in another farmhouse not far from Dmytro's.

"In the summer of 1943, we heard rumors that all the Jews in the surrounding towns had been killed by the Germans, and that those who had managed to escape were wandering the countryside, searching for places to hide. In our Sunday sermons, the priest said that our people should not hide the Jews because we all wanted a

Jew-free Ukraine after the war. Yet there were rumors that some of our people were hiding Jews, who gave them money or promised to give them their property after the war if they survived. My little brother told me that our mother had given some bread and milk to a woman carrying a baby who knocked on our window late at night but would not let her inside the house because she was afraid of our father. We also learned that in another village a Ukrainian police patrol found some Jews in a barn, killed them, and set fire to the house of the peasant who had allowed them to hide there. They threatened to kill him too but relented when he gave them the money he had got from the Jews. There were also more and more rumors that our OUN boys, whom everyone called Banderivtsy, were roaming the forests and preparing to fight both the Germans and the Soviets if they ever dared to return.

"By the beginning of 1944, most people thought that the Red Army would soon be back, and there were stories going around about a new Ukrainian insurgent army that was fighting for our independence. The more I heard about the insurgents' heroic actions, the more I wanted to leave the dreary farm work and join these liberators of Ukraine, but I didn't know how to make contact with them.

"Then I found out that Dmytro was hiding a Jewish family. One night I could not sleep and went outside. We had a bad case of lice, and they would not leave me in peace. My thoughts were taken up with how I could find the insurgents who were by then said to be in the forests around us. It was a bright night with an almost full moon and a clear sky. As I passed by Dmytro's house, his dog began to bark, but then it smelled me and calmed down. Just then I could hear a muffled cry, soon followed by another. It sounded as if the person uttering these cries had covered their mouth with something to stifle the sound. I was sure that the sound was coming from the Hutsul's house. Well, I said to myself, it's none of your business what he does there in the middle of the night. But my curiosity was awakened.

"Over the next few nights, I wandered around Dmytro's house a few more times. His dog had grown used to my visits and made no noise at all, and on the third or fourth night I again heard something. This time it was different, sounding more like a baby's cry. It instantly stopped, as if someone had put a hand over the baby's mouth. I was now quite sure that Dmytro was hiding Jews. His wife had given birth to twins shortly after the war began, but they were already four or five years old. The thought suddenly occurred to me that if I found a way to report this to the insurgents, who were known to be hunting down Jews wherever they operated, they might let me join them.

"I wondered why Dmytro would be hiding Jews. Did they give him money? He was still a young man with small children, so why would he want to risk their lives? I brushed that thought aside. The Jews had to be removed from our land. That was what the priest told us, that was what Stepan had preached to us, that was what the insurgents were now doing. After all our suffering, under the Poles, and the Soviets, and under the Germans, it was time for us to have our own land and be free of all foreigners and parasites. I thought that this would be my ticket to joining the insurgents. Then I would finally amount to something; with a gun and a uniform people would respect me. They would say, 'Look at Mykhailo the farmhand, now he is fighting for our liberation, he is our local hero.' These were the kinds of foolish thoughts that went through my mind at the time. I did not want to hurt Dmytro, who had been good to me, or his wife, who would occasionally bring some of her *kasza* to us farmworkers and on Sundays would treat us to *varenyky* with pork and mushrooms. She always greeted us with a smile, even when we were filthy and lice ridden. I hoped that nothing would happen to them. I would say that they were good people. It was just that the Jews had to be removed. Still, I was tormented by these thoughts.

"A couple of weeks later an entire German military unit entered the village. People said that these Waffen-SS troops were supposed to take up positions along the eastern bank of the Dniester and hold off advance units of the Red Army and local Soviet partisans, who were now also lurking in the forests. They installed their command post in the Grafina's abandoned villa. From this point on, the entire estate was filled with military vehicles and armed soldiers. We were allowed to continue working, because the Germans wanted our produce, but we were constantly bumping into these men from the SS. I envied their weapons and uniforms even though I was angry that they were taking away our milk and eggs and bread when we and the other villagers were starving.

"It occurred to me that sooner or later they were bound to find the family I was quite certain Dmytro was hiding somewhere in his house. That would mean that not only would the Jews be killed on the spot, but also Dmytro and his family and perhaps us farmworkers too, on suspicion that we had known about the Jews and failed to report them. By now we were familiar with the reputation of the SS and had little doubt about how brutal they could be. Still, they were polite with us and the rest of the village, and the company commander had invited Dmytro and the village head for drinks at the villa to introduce himself.

"The following Sunday, while making my way back from the church to the estate, I heard someone calling me from the edge of the forest. A man gestured for me to come closer and when I saw his face, I could not believe my eyes. Dressed in a combat uniform that was a mix of Red Army and Wehrmacht items, and armed with a pistol and a submachine gun, the man was none other than Stepan. When I told him that we had been sure he was dead, Stepan burst out laughing and said that he had managed to escape from the prison just before the executions began, and then joined the underground in the Lviv area. He had now been dispatched to our region to establish a local insurgent army unit.

"Years later, when I was already in England, I heard another story about Stepan. A veteran insurgent told me that after his arrest, Stepan agreed to collaborate with the NKVD, perhaps under torture, and denounced some of his own men. After the Soviets withdrew from Galicia, he joined the Ukrainian Auxiliary police that worked for the Germans. At some point in 1943, he deserted from the police and joined the insurgents, operated with them in Volhynia, where they cleansed many Polish villages, and then was sent to our region. This veteran told me that Stepan was eventually killed in a firefight with the Soviets, but that there were rumors that it was in fact not the NKVD that had killed him but one of his own men whom Stepan had denounced in 1941.

"I could not have known any of that when I met Stepan in the forest, although later on Dmytro stupidly said something similar. At that time, he was like a godsend. Here, finally, was my opportunity to join the insurgents and leave my wretched life on the farm behind. But Stepan was not the same man I had known a few years earlier. He wanted to ensure that all the fighters who joined his outfit were totally committed to the cause and to each other. The cause was the complete cleansing of Ukraine of all its enemies, and the way to ensure our total loyalty to each other was to prove that we would kill anyone he ordered us to. It was then that I told him about my suspicion that Dmytro was hiding a Jewish family on the estate. Stepan was incredulous. 'Even if that stupid Hutsul decided to take in a Jewish family,' he said, 'why would he keep them now when the whole place is crawling with SS?' He said that if the Hutsul was hiding Jews, we wouldn't be able to do anything about it anyway with so many Germans on the estate. He suggested that we inform the Germans. 'They'd take care of it in no time and finish off that Hutsul traitor just as quickly," he said. But to avoid making fools of ourselves, we first had to confirm that there were in fact Jews in hiding. This became my first mission. 'Let's find out how brave you really are,' Stepan chuckled.

"There were seven men in that outfit in addition to me and Stepan. Stepan ordered me to return to the farmworkers' quarters for the night so as not to raise any suspicions, and only after everyone was asleep find out where the Jews were hiding. Then I would meet the insurgents at the edge of the forest just before dawn. I did as Stepan had instructed me and spent the first part of the night tossing in bed and racking my brains about where the Jews might be hidden. There had been many stories in the region about Jews hiding on various farms. Some had been in holes dug out under stables or cowsheds. Others were in haylofts. Still others were discovered hiding in their host's homes behind stoves or behind false walls in their cellars.

"When everyone was sound asleep, I crept out, walked softly to the estate manager's house, lay down on the ground next to it, and carefully observed the surroundings. I had no watch but estimated the time to be well after midnight. The ground was very cold. It was March, and there were still patches of ice here and there. Dmytro's dog was trying to reach me, pulling on its chain. I was afraid it would begin making noise and crawled closer to it. The dog sniffed me and then sat down. Perhaps I should check out the barn first, I thought. As I prepared to crawl in that direction the dog growled, looking in the direction of the villa, where some lights could be seen in the windows.

"Then I heard the sound of a car engine starting up. In the distance I could hear voices. It sounded like they were barking orders. More lights went on in the windows of the villa. Now I could hear a heavy

142

truck rolling up the road from the village. What's going on? I thought. Are they preparing for some operation? Are the Russians already here? I felt unsafe sprawled on the ground in the middle of the yard and crawled quickly to the barn. The doors were bolted with a long wooden beam. I positioned myself at the corner, flat on the ground, and trained my eyes on the villa.

"The more I watched, the clearer it became that the Germans were packing up. The sky was becoming just a little lighter, and I could distinguish the tops of the trees against it. Another military vehicle had been positioned behind the big truck, its headlights serving to illuminate the space between them. I could see soldiers loading the truck with various objects brought from inside the villa. I remembered that I was supposed to meet Stepan and his men before dawn, but I could no longer move since the soldiers might notice me. If they did, they would shoot me on the spot. Gradually the darkness lifted and I could see that the Germans were ready to go. The commander came out of the villa and got into the car. He drove toward the village, where the rest of the unit was billeted, followed by the big truck. For a moment the sound of their engines filled the air. Then it grew still again. I looked around the yard. It was a beautiful spring morning, and birdsong filled the air. It was still very cold, though. A large butterfly was hovering close to the ground and then, perhaps carried by a light breeze, glided almost to the top of the barn. At that moment, I distinctly heard the cry of a baby, rapidly smothered. It almost certainly came from inside the barn. They are in the hayloft, I thought.

"'Go up there and take care of them,' I heard Stepan's baritone behind me. I turned around and there they were, the whole group, armed to the teeth. I jumped to my feet.

"'Can you handle this pistol?' Stepan handed me a German Luger. 'We'll make sure the Hutsul doesn't get in the way.'

"'Do you want me to kill them?' I asked, trying to sound as calm as I could.

"'Of course, why do you think we are here? Do you want to be a fighter or a stableboy?'

"'I've never fired a weapon in my life,' I answered, handing back the pistol.

"Then I heard the door of the estate manager's house open and saw Dmytro stepping out. He was holding his axe.

"'What are you doing on my property?' he called out. 'You'd better leave right now. And let go of that boy, too,' he added when he saw me behind Stepan's back.

"'You are hiding Jews here,' Stepan said calmly.

"'How dare you accuse me of that?' Dmytro responded. 'Do you think I'd hide Jews when the Germans are everywhere?'

"'Well,' said Stepan, 'now the Germans are gone, so you should have no worries about letting them go.'

"'I will do as I please on my property,' Dmytro answered and started walking toward us, the wide blade of his axe glittering in the early morning sun. 'I know who you are,' he said to Stepan as he came closer. 'You are that no-good bastard who squealed about your own people to the Bolsheviks, and now you are playing at being a hero again.'

"Two shots rang out and Dmytro fell lifelessly to the ground, still holding his axe.

"'You should really learn how to use this Luger,' Stepan said, observing his pistol. 'The Germans make damn good weapons. But since you can't use firearms, you'd better take the axe. I'm sure you know how to handle that.'

144

"I walked over to Dmytro's slumped body. His head was a bloody mess. You could not see his face. In the distance I could hear someone shrieking. It must be Oksana, I thought. I felt nothing, as if my insides had frozen. The other guys were joking around, making fun of that stupid peasant and his axe. He was holding on to it so tightly that I had difficulty extracting it from his hand. Finally, I stood up, holding the axe in both hands. It was a beautiful tool with a large, broad blade, and an intricately carved wooden handle, now spattered with Dmytro's blood.

"Oksana was screaming my name in the distance.

"'Go over there and shut that woman up,' Stepan said to one of his men. 'Now get on with it, we don't have all day,' he said, turning to me. He was still holding the Luger, tilting it this way and that, as if to see whether it was well balanced.

"I walked over to the barn door and pulled out the wooden bar. A couple of shots rang out behind me, and Oksana's screams now turned into something I had never heard before, like cries from a wild beast whose limbs were being torn apart.

"'You can go and play too, boys,' Stepan said to the other men. 'I'll keep watch over this stableboy.'

"I walked into the dark barn. It was cooler inside and smelled of manure and fresh hay. I let my eyes get used to the darkness and saw a ladder at the far end, its top part leaning onto the hayloft. I slowly approached it. Just before I reached it, someone leaped at me from behind a bundle of hay. I swung at him with the axe and heard a dull sound as the blade hit his head. He died without a whimper. It was a middle-aged man, quite thin. He had no shoes on and smelled of urine, excrement, and sweat. I had literally split his head in half. In the light increasingly streaming into the barn from the narrow openings at the top I could see a pair of round glasses on the floor a few feet from him. I stuck the handle of the axe into my belt and climbed slowly up the ladder.

"All I could see were piles of hay scattered all over. I reached up to the low ceiling and opened one of the hatches to let in more light. Now I could distinguish the figure of a woman in the far corner. She was hunched over a little bundle and appeared to be silently weeping. Her long hair was filled with bits of straw. Just as I raised the axe she cried out, '*Loyf, loyf!*' I could hear little steps behind me and as I turned around, I saw a little girl scurrying down the ladder. The woman was now on her feet. She tried to grab the axe, but I pushed her away. She stumbled back, hitting her head on one of the beams supporting the roof, and then collapsed silently onto the floor. I looked at the bundle. The baby was blue and did not seem to be breathing. She must have smothered it while trying to keep it quiet. I looked out the little window on the side of the hayloft and saw the girl running across the meadow. Then a shot rang out and she fell.

"Stepan was calling me from below, 'Come down already, we don't have all day!' As I walked back to the ladder, I felt something under my foot. I bent down and picked it up. It looked like a little notebook filled with scribbles in a script I had never seen before.

"'Did you finish the job?' Stepan shouted.

"'They are all dead,' I replied.

"'Did you find any money or gold there?'

"'No, there's nothing up here,' I said, and stuck the little notebook into my pocket.

"When I walked out of the barn, Stepan and the other men were getting ready to leave. The men's clothes were stained with blood, and they were making jokes about the Hutsul's wife. 'We found a nice bundle there,' one of them said. 'The Jews must have given these pigs all they had.'

"'Alright,' Stepan said, 'it's time for breakfast. You,' he turned to me, 'clean up the mess here. Get them all into the barn and burn it down. Then you can join us. We'll even have some vodka for you.' He did not say where I should meet them, and I did not ask. They walked off and disappeared in the forest.

"The sun was quite high by now, but it was still chilly. I was sweating profusely. I walked over to the estate manager's house. Oksana was sprawled on the floor. The lower part of her body was naked, and her legs were smeared with blood. Her face was distorted into a horrifying grin. They must have strangled her. The two toddlers had been tossed to one of the corners of the room, both shot to death. I wiped the blood off the blade of the axe with the end of my shirt and hung it over the fireplace. Then I dragged Oksana's body to the barn, went back to the house, wrapped the children in the tablecloth from the dinner table and deposited them next to their mother. As I walked across the meadow toward the little girl's body, a vast cloud of butterflies rose from the ground and hovered over her like a multicolored blanket. I carried her in my arms to the barn, and the butterflies followed us. I wanted to put her together with her mother and father and the baby, but I could not bring myself to do it. By now I was feeling quite delirious. I brought a can of kerosene from the toolshed and drenched the interior and walls of the barn. Then I rolled myself a cigarette, lit it, and threw the match into the barn. It was completely engulfed in flames by the time I reached the edge of the forest.

"My dear grandson, Andriy. I know this will come as a shock to you, but I must tell you that after this event, I never joined the insurgents, even though that had always been my most cherished dream. I never went to meet Stepan and his men, and never came back to the village or my family. The Red Army was not far, and although it was driven back by the Germans for a while, it took over the entire region that summer. I ended up joining a transport that was taking thousands of Poles, villagers and townspeople alike, who were escaping our insurgents and the bitter fighting between the Germans and the Russians.

"The Germans showed no mercy as they retreated. They looted, burned, and destroyed everything in their way. They wanted to make it more difficult for the Red Army to sustain itself and recruit new soldiers from the population. Our insurgents used this opportunity to raid one Polish village after another, killing and burning, so that the Poles would understand that this was not their land but ours and flee to the West. I saw the results of these horrors on the train, where I was pretending to be one of those Poles. The boxcars were crammed with people who had lost everything, their husbands and wives, mothers and fathers, children and parents, people who had been shot, slashed, burned, and tortured, people who had gone mad from grief and fear and pain. I had never seen so much human misery in my life and just wanted to get away from it all as soon as I could.

"My dear grandson, as I so often told you, since I was a boy, I had always wanted to join the patriots who were fighting to liberate Ukraine from its oppressors. I also wanted to liberate myself from the oppression of my own circumstances. The future appeared so bleak for a young lad from a peasant family working as a farmhand on an isolated estate. But I did not tell you that what I experienced that day on the estate cured me forever from any desire to fight. That day, as I made my way through the forest, heading to the bridge across the Dniester and then on to Stanyslaviv, I felt as if everything had drained out of me; every emotion, every desire had just been sucked out of me, and all that was left was an overwhelming horror at what I had seen, what I had done, what I had become. I vomited repeatedly, but felt no hunger and no thirst, just nausea and disgust. My hands were trembling and my eyes were burning. When I wiped my forehead with the end of my shirt, I realized I was smearing blood on my face, the blood from the blade of the axe. I wanted to pray but did not know how. It was a brilliant day, I remember that very clearly; sparkling blue skies, the fresh smell of the forest coming to life after a long winter, the soft feel of the forest floor covered with pine needles and patches of snow. But my heart was empty.

"In Stanyslaviv, I stayed for a few hours in a vast refugee encampment and then boarded a train to Poland. We could hear the artillery booming in the East and saw bombers and fighter planes flying this way and that. Bombs were dropped on the city and near the train station, but we managed to leave unscathed. It was a long train journey, the boxcar full of exhausted and ill people sitting on the floor surrounded by their bundles. I was afraid to fall asleep, because every time I shut my eyes, I heard the dull thud of the axe crushing the man's skull, I smelled the blood smeared on my face, I saw the barn engulfed in flames, and over it all butterflies were silently flapping their wings. I spent months in refugee camps in Lublin, then in Łódź, and at the end of the war found myself in the Villach displaced persons camp in the British zone in Austria.

"This, as I have told you many times in the past, was where I met and married your grandmother Yana, who had been deported from her village. She had been sent to work in a factory in Klagenfurt, near Villach, where she was liberated at the end of the war. I never told her about the events on the estate, nor have I ever told your father. It is up to you to decide if you want to tell him. You are a historian and have a better understanding of things than he does. He has never liked my preoccupation with our veterans.

"In the early years, when Taras was a child, I would often take him to parades, and picnics, and later also to the balls for former insurgents. I told many tall tales about my days of fighting with them, about my feats as an insurgent. They were all made up, inspired by the stories of other veterans I had heard and read. No one ever suspected it was all lies. Maybe I was not the only liar. It made life more meaningful for us. Many of the men who came from Ukraine to England lived very humble lives. I never made it out of working as a farmer. I was always a peasant, like my father before me and his father before him and all our ancestors since time immemorial. Only your father managed to move up a bit, and you, my talented grandson, made it all the way to Oxford.

"I think you know that I did try to educate myself when I could find the time and energy. It began because I needed to know as much as possible about those years. I sometimes think that those who lie must know much more than those who tell the truth, because they need to imagine what others simply remember, and what they imagine must appear as true as if they truly did remember it. I came to understand that in inventing one's own life, one learns by reading about other invented lives. Perhaps one learns more about truth through fiction than history, because fiction, at least the kind of literature I was reading, tells you about human beings like yourself, and not about all those generals and leaders that historians and newspapers write about.

"It was then that I discovered our writer Ivan Franko, who came from a village not that far from our own. And it was from his stories about the world that I came from that I began to grasp that world, which I remembered but could never understand or know how to describe. He painted it with his words and made it possible for me, in my own limited way, to write about it, as I had always wanted but never did, in this letter to you, my dearest grandchild. It was Franko who taught me how to write, and also Shevchenko, that rebellious serf whose divine verses moved me to tears when they echoed in my memories of that life of poverty and despair I had so longed to leave, and the horror of that departure that will never be erased.

"Sometimes, my dear Andriy, especially as I grew older, I would ask myself, how many of these aging men did what I did that day on the estate? How many of them were like Stepan, who must have bathed in blood up to his ears? They were jolly old men, and proud of their deeds, and when our country was liberated from the Bolsheviks and became independent again, there was no end to our joy. But what about the truth? Did we ever face up to it? Maybe one day you, as a scholar, the historian I had always hoped you would become, will be able to write about all this with the right kind of objectivity and dispassion. We could not.

"There is one last thing I must mention here, because you are a historian, but also because not a day has gone by without me thinking about it. I did not know the Jews in the barn, but I recognized them. They were old Szumer's daughter, her husband, and their daughter. She must have had the baby while in hiding. That was probably what I heard that night; those muffled cries from Dmytro's house. But what I wanted to mention to you in these closing lines is what happened to that little notebook I found in the barn. I carried it in my pocket for a long time, through refugee camps and displaced persons camps, and it always felt like something burning my chest through the fabric of my jacket. I did not know what to do with it and at times I thought that I should just throw it away, but something stopped me. Maybe I wanted to atone for what I had done.

"One day in Villach, I got talking with a middle-aged Jewish man. He spoke good Ukrainian and told me that he came from a village in Galicia, where his father had owned a tavern before the war. His father was killed by the villagers when the Russians left, but he somehow survived, and was about to go to Palestine to start a new life. I told him that I had found a notebook on the estate in which I

151

worked, and that it must have been left behind by the Jews who had been hiding there. I did not mention what happened to them although for a moment, facing this Jewish man, with the notebook burning my chest like a flame, I came close to confessing. 'We helped them as much as we could,' I said, 'but when the Germans set up a command post near their hiding place, they escaped, and I do not know what happened to them. The notebook is written in a script I cannot read.' The man said he didn't know what to do with it, but suggested I speak to someone in the camp sent by the Jewish Historical Commission to collect evidence about the mass killings of the Jews.

"The next day I met this man, a young and energetic fellow who spoke only Polish. Luckily my Polish was good enough to be able to communicate with him. I told him the same story about finding the notebook in Myryn and mentioned that the only words I could decipher were on the cover, where the name Judit Reichert was written in Roman letters. It was harder for me to part with this notebook than I had expected, but I finally took it out of my pocket and handed it to the man, whose name I can no longer remember. He looked at it and said that it was written in Hebrew, probably by a child judging by the writing. 'What will you do with it?' I asked.

"'We collect thousands of testimonies from Jews who have survived the slaughter,' he answered, 'and will deposit them in an institute in Warsaw so that historians in the future will be able to use these materials to write the history of what happened. This notebook could serve as one of the building blocks of that history,' he added, sensing my reluctance to part with it. 'As long as you have the name of the person who wrote it and the place in which it was written, it should not be difficult for you to locate it in the archive we are building if you ever wish to. I will also add a note to say that the notebook was donated by you.' But I decided not to give him my name.

"I handed him the notebook. I have never sought to find it, and there were periods in my life when I completely forgot about it. But having

152

written you this account, I now hope that you will be able to find it, or at least tell its story to someone who might be interested, because it is the last record of a family that no longer exists and should not be consigned to oblivion. By the time you read this, I will no longer be alive. But I would like to think that you recovered the notebook and whatever this little girl might have written there. I apologize for having burdened you with my story. I expect you will never think of me as you used to. I have done bad things for which I was not punished, though I did live an unhappy life to the end. I hope that you have a happier and more fulfilled life, free of the crimes and lies of the past, and of the suspicion and resentment that cloud your father's life. You are still a young man, and the future belongs to you. Make of it what you will, but never forget what came before, and never forget who you are, a good and smart man, a loyal British citizen, and a proud Ukrainian. Your loving grandfather, Mykhailo."

JUDIT

Mykhailo's confession, if that is what it was, left me with mixed feelings. He had confided in his grandson, albeit from beyond the grave, and sought to make right the lies and obfuscations of his life. I thought that even then, he had attempted to stay in Andriy's good graces. During his lifetime, Mykhailo had described himself as a heroic freedom fighter who was never truly compensated for his sacrifice and had been forced to flee his homeland and live in anonymity and poverty in a foreign land. Now he had created a new posthumous identity for himself, in which he confessed his complicity in a crime and admitted that he had never been that heroic insurgent he had always wanted to be. Once again, he presented himself as a victim of circumstances and misfortune.

Even as he conceded complicity in murder, it appeared from his account that he had not actually murdered anyone. True, he had killed Max with an axe, but that was in self-defense as Max attacked him first, trying to defend his family. As for Rochaleh, he had only pushed her when she tried to grab his axe, which resulted in her accidentally hitting her head on a beam. She may not actually have been dead at that point, perishing only later, when he set fire to the barn. The baby was suffocated by its own mother in her frantic attempt to silence it when she heard the insurgents in the yard. As for little Judit, Mykhailo seemed to imply that he had let her run away, and that she had been shot by the murderous Stepan. One would also have to take him at his word that he had nothing to do with the rape and murder of Oksana, Dmytro's wife, or with the killing of their twins. Having depicted the brutality of the insurgents, his admission that he never actually joined them could be seen in a very different light, as a refusal to take part in more such crimes. Perhaps it was revulsion at such murderous tactics rather than cowardice; whichever it was, Mykhailo subsequently concealed it under a facade of jolly participation in nationalist ceremonies with real veterans of that futile and bloody insurgency.

My skepticism was tempered by the tone and tenor of the confession. Initially, I wondered whether a man with so little education, who had spent his entire life as a farmer, could have written such a text, and I suspected that Andriy polished or even modified it somewhat when translating it. But since I was acquainted with the writings of Ivan Franko, and similarly familiar with the emotional and at times violent poetry of Taras Shevchenko, I could imagine that Mykhailo's love for these icons of Ukrainian letters must have had some influence on his prose. Mostly, I felt that if Mykhailo did not perhaps tell the whole truth, in part because he might have wanted to spare his grandson some of the more gruesome details, there was nonetheless a truth in this document that ran deeper than these possible obfuscations. It was written, I thought, by a man who had been ground down his entire life by what occurred on that chilly morning in March 1944, and whose inability to face up to that past, perhaps fueled by his desire to protect his family from what he had done, had irreparably damaged his relationship with his son and made for a bond rooted in untruth and pretense with his grandson, whom he clearly loved deeply. "The fathers have eaten sour grapes, and the children's teeth are set on edge," I found myself saying. I had always heard this verse growing up. I looked it up in Jeremiah. It was followed by another verse I had not remembered, prophesying that one day, every man that eats sour grapes, his teeth shall be set on edge. Perhaps, I thought; but would that put an end to it?

Andriy had asked Tali if she knew how Judit's notebook could be located, and Tali had in turn asked me. Was there any point in looking for it? Would we learn something from it we would otherwise never know about that event 75 years ago? It struck me that most people were not interested in how their relatives had died in the Holocaust. They would say, so and so many members of my family perished. But how? They were murdered by the Nazis and their collaborators. Is that enough? Don't we want to know more than that? If their lives were so precious, at least to us, as we claim, even if we never knew them, should we not want to know the circumstances of their murder? Is that not why we have courts and trials, witnesses and judges? Have we given up on trying to find out or did we never really want to know in the first place, preferring to wrap it all in vague pronouncements about innocents and martyrs, evildoers and perpetrators? Do we want to protect ourselves from what we may find, the sordid reality of snuffing out an individual life?

Judit's notebook, I thought, even if we could locate it, would likely tell us nothing about these events. Whatever musings a 10-year-old girl might have jotted down, they would not have included the details of her murder. Perhaps that was for the better, I finally concluded.

A few days after reading Mykhailo's confession, I contacted my old research assistant, Ulrich Ackermann, to seek his help in locating the notebook. I have known Uli for three decades, and he is only a few years younger than me. He grew up and was educated in East Germany, and perhaps because of that, as well as his innate nature, he has always been somewhat diffident despite his towering physique and handsome features. His career, like that of many other young East German academics, was derailed by reunification. With a PhD from the communist era, he could never find a job in the newly expanded Federal Republic, while academics trained in West

Germany streamed into newly available slots at universities in the former German Democratic Republic.

Uli has unmatched skills as an archival researcher, and over the years I was one of the beneficiaries of his investigative prowess. Along the way, we became friends, and I spent some time vacationing with his family in his wife's homeland of Poland, staying in a rather monastic guesthouse on the Baltic shore, sauntering to the beach and enjoying traditional Polish suppers uncannily like my mother's cooking but for the pork. Living on the border between the two countries, they seem unable to decide where they would rather be, or perhaps enjoy the benefits of both. Uli is fluent in Polish, Ukrainian, and Russian, while his wife teaches German in a Polish school across the river. Their children, like mine, have had their difficulties growing up with parents tracing themselves back to other lands, some of which no longer exist, at least not in the same guise.

As I expected, all it took Uli to solve the mystery was a train ride to Warsaw and half a day's work in the archives of the Jewish Historical Institute. The notebook was filed under its place of origin and the name of its author. There was nothing else under the placename Mierzyn/Myryn, save for an intriguing letter by a certain Antosia Majewska of Wrocław, originally from the village of Wyszkowce in the district of Zakłócenie, sent in August 1947 to the Central Jewish Committee in Warsaw, appealing for financial assistance.

"In 1943," she wrote, "I selflessly helped a Jewish child from Zakłócenie after the Judenrein by the Germans. I hid her for several months in my own home, provided her with hot meals, protected her from the Germans and local bandits, refused to divulge her whereabouts under beatings and threats to my life and property, and helped her reach her parents in the village of Mierzyn. I do not know what became of the girl and her parents, but if they survived, I am certain they will confirm my testimony. Their names are Max and Rachela Reichert, and their girl is called Judit. Now I have been evicted from my home as a Pole and find myself in dire circumstances in a dilapidated apartment with no income and failing health." Majewska asked for financial help to open a shop as a means to obtain a stable income. There was no confirmation of whether she had ever received that help.

Despite his linguistic skills, when Uli finally discovered the notebook, tucked away in a large brown envelope and described as "Recollections from the village of Mierzyn," all he could read was the name on the cover. In the email he sent me that night from his hotel in Warsaw, which included an attachment with the scanned contents of the notebook, he wrote in German, "Here is what I think you were looking for. As far as I can tell, the notebook, or perhaps the diary, is written in Hebrew. It is in a rather fragile condition because of the quality of the paper and because the writing in pencil is quite faint. But you will be able to enhance that on your computer. I am very glad we were able to find this document. You did not say so directly, but I sensed that this may concern your own family. I suppose you could say that this is a voice from the obscurity to which your family was consigned by the German murderers. I hope it will be useful to you. Warm greetings to you and the family." Uli did not include an invoice this time and refused payment when I proposed to cover his costs. I promised to send him my English translation of the notebook in due course.

Although I had spent years reading such accounts, this document was especially difficult, both because of its emotional content and because parts of it were confusing. Only on a second reading did I figure out that after surviving the German occupation with her parents in Zakłócenie for almost two years, in spring 1943 Judit was taken into hiding in the nearby village of Wyszkowce by the Polish peasant Antosia Majewska. Initially accompanied by another Jewish woman named Sala Dobrecka, who later disappeared and was probably killed, Judit was then left alone with her protectors. While she was sheltered by several Polish women, Judit was constantly threatened by Antosia's Ukrainian brother-in-law, Danylo, who may also have sexually abused her. The last section of the diary recounts Judit's reunion with her parents in her mother's village of Mierzyn. Judit only began writing this diary after rejoining her parents, first as an account of what she had experienced up to that point and then as diary entries during the spring of 1944. Each part reflects Judit's state of mind. The first section, about her time in Zakłócenie with her parents, is clear and succinct. The second reflects Judit's state of constant terror and is fragmented and disjointed. The last section is written as real-time diary entries ending just moments before the family's murder. Here it is.

"I am writing this diary in Hebrew because I no longer ever want to use any other language. Father taught me Hebrew at home and sent me to the Tarbut school. Hebrew is hard to write but uses fewer letters than Polish so my pencil will not run out as quickly. May it be like the miracle of the little can of olive oil we celebrate in Hanukkah, which lasted eight days. I am now with my parents in the village where my mother was born. I have decided to write this diary because there is nothing to do in the hayloft. Oksana is very kind to us. She gave me a pencil and some paper. I will first write what happened before I came here. I asked Father to tell me what he knows about the murder of our people in Zakłócenie so I can record it. If they find us, I will hide the diary and maybe one day someone will discover it and know who we were and what happened to us. I am sorry if I make spelling mistakes, but Father can correct them after I finish writing. For now, I will not show my diary to anyone. Writing will help me think less about being afraid all the time, and about my whole body aching because we cannot move in the hayloft. We can only come down at night to stretch our limbs.

"One month after the Germans came to our town the Jews had to register. Father went along. Of the Jews gathered there, only those who had special professions in town were released. Father was sent home because he was a miller. The rest (350 men, Father said) were shot. For several months it was quiet. We were given bread. And then we heard that roundups had taken place in the neighboring towns. We knew that within a short time there would be one against us as well. Some people built hiding places. Everyone remained in hiding at night. Later people stopped talking about a roundup and did not hide any longer. And precisely then the first roundup took place in November 1942. Father fled to the forest. I was in hiding at the neighbors' place. Mother was with Grandfather and Grandmother in our cellar. We always hid in different places, so that at least one of our family would survive. After the roundup, Father said that 1,500 people had been deported, and that 250 were shot in the streets.

"After a month, all the Jews from the neighboring areas were sent to us. In the Jewish houses, it became very crowded. There was typhus everywhere, and many people died. I think 30 died every day. We were allowed to live only in the worst part of town.

"In December 1942, there was a second roundup. Father said that 1,500 people were taken away. Sick people were shot in their beds. Only those who had hidden remained alive, as well as the Jewish Council and the Jewish Police. The Jewish Police helped the Germans a lot.

"In January 1943, people began to dig ditches. Father guessed that they were graves, and other people, who did not want to believe this, found other explanations. I remember that then it was quiet again, there was no panic and it looked like we would be able to live normally. But Father was always sad and spoke about the ditches. I heard 'how he spoke with Grandfather about sending me to a village in the countryside. But it was very difficult to get out of the city.

"The third roundup was in February 1943. My grandmother was killed in this roundup. She was discovered in a bunker together with 51 other people, and she was shot next to the trenches that had been prepared in advance. In this roundup 1,500 were killed, and many were also shot in the street. My parents and I were in hiding.

"After this roundup a camp was built in the town, but people had to pay to be in it. Everyone else was taken to other towns and killed there. Father went into the camp and Mother and I lived in the city next to the camp. The camp was surrounded by barbed wire and guarded by the Jewish Police. The Gestapo visited the camp from time to time. The camp inmates tilled the land in the camp and did chores for the Aryans in the city. One Saturday before Passover 1943, the Gestapo seized about 50 women and children who lived outside the camp and shot them.

"My mother and I were hiding in a bunker under the floor. After that roundup we lived only in the bunker, along with our neighbors. Father brought food from the camp. It was calm, and mother even whitewashed the hiding place for the holidays. Then the fourth roundup occurred. Another 1,500 people were taken, mainly women and children. I remember one case, a family of people we knew were hiding in a bunker with a three-year-old child. When the police came close to the bunker, the child began to cry, and the mother smothered it. This mother poisoned herself later.

"Several days after this roundup, on Saturday evening, the Polish peasant woman Antosia, who sometimes brought us milk from her village, came to us and took me and Mrs. Sala Dobrecka with her. She received a plush coat from my parents. We left at night without even saying goodbye to my father because we thought we would come back. We went through fields and woods because we were afraid of walking on the road. After an hour, we came to a miserable, gloomy stable where we were given a ladder to climb into the hayloft. Dobrecka climbed first and I followed her. At the top it was dark. We slept under a duvet, and then it was morning. When the sun rose, Antosia brought us *kasza* and went back to town. When she returned, she brought me a letter from my parents, who were fine. A few days passed. Antosia again went to town and brought me a bad letter. Mama wrote that the day before yesterday they had been in great danger and that death was constantly stalking them. We were saddened by this news. She wrote that Father was looking for a shelter. The next day Antosia went to town and returned with the news that my parents had left. I didn't know what to think at this point, so I wrote to my father to take pity on me and save me.

"Antosia said to Sala Dobrecka that she should go, and that I would leave in the evening. Sala took a bag with her and left. I was alone now. The moon shone sadly. The next night somebody was walking outside. Sala was coming. When Antosia heard noises, she came out. She got scared when she saw Sala. Sala gave me an address in Palestine and promised to bring me photos of my parents. Antosia didn't want to hear any of it and told Sala to go away. Antosia's brother-in-law, Danylo, came and took down the duvet and Sala climbed down. I hid in the stable behind the doors, but Sala left. This was a terrible moment for me. The next day Danylo came to the hayloft, but I don't know what he was doing. He put his hands on me and asked, 'Have the Germans tried to kill you already?' He said, 'Tomorrow I'll be going to town to hunt down Jews.' At that moment, I wanted to die. He left and I was weeping. Then Antosia climbed up, but I said nothing.

"A few days passed calmly, but I had no news from my parents. On Wednesday, Danylo climbed up to the hayloft. He was very drunk, and he didn't know what he was saying. He asked, 'Who is your father? What do your parents belong to?' Another two days passed in peace, and then Antosia went to town and brought news that a sixth roundup was taking place, and I was very despondent. She brought my dinner and left. I covered myself with a blanket and a scarf and fell asleep. At midnight, I heard someone walking outside. I got up as I felt that something bad was going to happen to me. But I could not think of what to do. Danylo climbed up to the hayloft and strangled me. He said, 'Give me money or I will report you.' Then Antosia and her sister climbed up and let me down from the hayloft through another opening. I climbed down in the dark and ran to the courtyard, to a hole full of beets, and crawled in under them. I felt that my leg was bleeding. Antosia gave me the blanket and the scarf, and I climbed out of the hole and ran to the toolshed. But she ordered me to go back to the hayloft. When I reached the hayloft, I didn't know what was happening to me. Antosia said that at night she would lock me in.

"The next day, Antosia went to Bogdan in town, and he gave her a letter from my parents. She gave me the letter and I was very happy. Mama wrote to me that everything was fine; they had just built a bunker, and they still hoped to see me again. That day the Germans came to the village, and I ran away to the potato field. I heard gunshots. They killed six Jews who were staying with the Kowalski family, and I was very despondent. A neighbor who was walking in his field spotted me. Antosia came and took me back from the field. But Danylo was drunk. I ran away to another field. Antosia went to her aunt to ask if she would hide me, and she agreed. In the evening, she brought me a long skirt. I put it on and went to the field. Antosia gave me a liter of milk and buttered bread and covered me with sheaves of hay, and I stayed there. The field was 8 kilometers from the village and quite large. During the day, the woman who owned it was working there and I was happy. On Thursday, I wanted to fast. At night it rained. There was a thunderstorm and strong lightening and I got so wet that my bag of money got soaked. I cried from cold and fear. Soon it was morning. I heard footsteps. The owner came. She brought me milk kasza. I finished eating and felt better and she left.

"Four days passed this way. During this time, Antosia built a partition for me in the hayloft. When I came back to the village, she said that she would take me to the hayloft but that no one should know. I climbed up to the hayloft where the partition had been built. I spent a whole week there. Whenever Danylo left, she fed me. Once on a Friday, I took off my shoes and my coat and fell asleep. Suddenly I heard someone walking in boots in the courtyard. I was sure it was Danylo because no one else would wear boots in the summer. He opened the door of the stable, walked in, placed the ladder by the hayloft, climbed up, put his head and hands to the part of the hayloft that was partitioned, and then left the stable. Right away I threw down two bundles of hay and jumped down on them. I ran to the cornfield. Someone crossed my path. I thought it was Danylo, but he didn't come after me. It was very cold and there was a lot of dew. I lay there all wet until the morning. In the afternoon I called out and Antosia took me back to the stable. She didn't want to keep me anymore. She said, 'What do you think? You keep running off, who knows where. Someone will see you, and then what will happen?' But she brought me a tub of water and I washed myself. I climbed to the hayloft.

"Antosia went to her aunt Różka to ask if she would take me to her field. But she could not do that because the stalks were not yet high enough to hide in. Różka took me to someone else's field. During those two days it rained, and I was covered with a blanket. Różka gave me some *pierogi* and water, and I lay down on the bundles of hay. After two days, she took me back to her stable in the evening, where she and her sister slept with me. Różka had an ethnic German daughter-in-law who did not know about me. Before daybreak I went to the field to lie in the corn until evening, and at night I went back to the stable. In that field I was very afraid because the daughter-in-law liked to walk there.

"Then it began to rain, and it went on for several days. I couldn't lie in the field, but only in the stable, where I covered myself with hay.

164

The aunt couldn't bring me any food and I could not go out. When Antosia found out about this she made me a long skirt for my money. She came to fetch me and took me to her house at noon but ordered me to come to the stable in the evening. When I came, Danylo was shouting and Antosia was tearing her hair out. When she saw me, she said that she would kill herself. She ordered me to go to the hole in the ground and to lie there until midnight. After that, things calmed down. They went to sleep and Antosia came and talked to me about her own life until it got light outside. At dawn, she took me to her aunt's stable. I stayed there one more day, and then she said she would take me to the hole. I would be in the hole during the day and in the hayloft at night. I agreed to this. At night, she slept with me in the hayloft. Finally, I was happy.

"Then came harvest time. Danylo did not go to work, only to the harvest. They went to the field, and Antosia fed the cow and gave me food. I lived in this manner in the hole for two weeks until Danylo's wife, Jaga, spotted me and ordered me to go to the hayloft as she was afraid that I would catch tuberculosis. Danylo found out I was there. Time passed very quietly. Danylo wasn't drinking. He had nothing to do with me. In the morning, Antosia brought me soup and bread. I ate and began knitting a sweater. Antosia brought me yarn. At night Antosia slept with me and talked to me. I stayed in the hayloft for four weeks. It rained, so I got soaked.

"One evening, Antosia told me that a roundup against the Poles was taking place. Suddenly, I heard shots and climbed down to the stable. I hid behind the door and Antosia's sister came in and was frightened by me. I cried out, 'Spare me!' She ordered me to go back to the hayloft. The next day was a holiday. The whole family went and only she stayed behind. She brought me meat soup and *kasza* with meat. She sat next to me for about an hour and urged me to eat. She told me that those who eat non-kosher food would live and those who eat kosher would not. But I was not convinced. Then she brought me *kasza* with raw milk. We spoke a little, and she left. I remained alone.

"At night, the dog always slept, but every time he stirred, I thought someone was coming. Once in the evening, Antosia came and brought me two hats and consoled me, saying that in two days she would take me to her home. At her place in the yard there were chickens of many breeds. I made a hole in the roof and when no one was there I would look at the chickens and think that soon I would be free. One time the Germans came to requisition provisions from the farm. On that day people were cleaning beets. The Germans came to the yard and entered the house, and I was staring death in the face. I hid under a plank of wood and covered myself with straw. When they entered the stable, they climbed up to the other side of the hayloft. At that point I did not stop beseeching God. They didn't find anything and went back to the yard. Toward evening, Antosia brought me cooked *kasza* with milk without a spoon. I didn't want her to go back to bring me a spoon, so I ate with the crust of bread. The next day, Antosia came and consoled me by saying that the following week she would take me to her house. I spent that week in peace.

"One night, I woke up and heard someone in the hayloft. It was Danylo, and he started calling out, 'Judit!' I fainted from fear. He called again, 'Judit, Judit, don't be afraid.' I said to him, 'Let me go, otherwise I will die.' He said to me, 'Don't worry, I just wanted to know if you were there. I am going back.' I said, 'Go away.' He began to move and just then I heard Jaga and Antosia in the hayloft. I went down by the ladder to the stable, opened the door, and ran out into the yard. I had no place to hide because there were lights in the neighbors' houses. I bent over and crawled into a pile of hay. Through a gap I could see that it was dark. I was afraid and shivering from cold and hunger. Suddenly I was overcome with fear and crawled out. The moon was not shining and there were no stars—it was pitch-black. I went through the orchard because I was afraid to walk on the main road. I came to a pigsty but could not enter it because all the openings were covered with corn leaves. I had no way to get in; there were dogs in the yard, and I was afraid. Then it occurred to me to lift the corn leaves and go inside. I lay down in the hay.

"Finally, it was morning and Różka came. She told me that Antosia was dying and she wondered who would look after me. I asked her what had happened, and she told me that yesterday evening Danylo had hit Antosia on the head with a stick from the shed and cracked her skull. Today she went to the hospital in the city. She asked me what she could bring me to eat, and I said that I was fasting. In the afternoon she brought me beans and bread. I did not want to eat because I was fasting and only begged God that Antosia would live. The next day Różka brought milk *kasza* and *pierogi*. I ate and gave her the dish back. On Sunday everyone went to Zaklots and only Różka's sister stayed behind. She brought me an oil lamp and a comb. Later, she came and brought me *pierogi* with cheese and with onion. I ate and began to comb my hair with oil. After brushing she began to tell me about her life. She told me how she suffered because her son beats and abuses her. Suddenly I heard shouts. A neighbor was beating his wife. She stopped talking and went out to see what was happening. I started to think about the future.

"The next day in the evening, Antosia came to me and said that for winter I'll go to her place, but no one should know apart from her. I should give her 10 złoty to buy bread and there will be nothing else to eat. She would take me in two weeks. During these two weeks, I was unhappy. Staszek was cleaning the stable and flipped over the hay on which I slept at night [thus discovering that someone was hiding there]. Różka said to me that she was going to report me and that I should pray to God. I thought that either I would be saved, or I would not. In the evening the rest of the family talked with Różka and said that it would be best if I left of my own free will, because otherwise people would find out about me. Antosia told me that she would take me to her house until the Soviets arrived. I went through the orchard to her place, entered the stable, and climbed into the hayloft. It was so full of straw that there was no room to move, so I lay down next to the entrance. In the morning she came to milk the cow and gave me a mug of milk. I had my own bread, so I cut off a slice and ate. Three times a day she gave me milk. Danylo did not drink anymore, so I lived in peace. I thought only about when I would be free.

"Several weeks passed without any water. I did not wash even once, and I combed my hair only every two weeks. I had no room to raise my arms. My thoughts at the time were only on how I would be free to go to Eretz Israel and to build the land and no longer remain in the Diaspora. One evening the hay came loose, and I wanted to tie it up. Danylo was in the stable and heard; I noticed him only as he was leaving. I thought I would kill myself. I was sure that he would get drunk, and things would go badly for me. In the morning, Antosia came, and I told her that he had heard me. She began to curse, saying how she suffered because of me and said that she would throw me out and I could go wherever I wanted. We needed to wait to see at what time he would come home in the evening. If he came late, he would be drunk.

"Finally evening arrived, but Danylo did not come. She milked the cow and gave me milk. She was angry, and she left. Suddenly someone pushed open the door and entered. It was Antosia. 'Run away right now!' she cried. I climbed down from the hayloft and went outside. There was snow, wind and frost, a terrible storm. It was stinging my ears, it was awful. Just then I saw opposite me a Ukrainian militiaman; I had nowhere to run, but I noticed a pile of snow in the yard, and I crept under it. It was where the straw was kept in the summer. I had no socks, only shoes. Antosia feared that I would freeze so she came to me and said that I should go back to the hayloft, because if I died it would be impossible to bury me in the frozen earth. But I didn't want to. I said that Danylo would come at night, break open the padlock and go straight at me. I lay in the pile of snow and listened. Morning arrived. Antosia brought me milk and bread. I ate, and he still wasn't there. In the evening, he came back sober and said that he had not come back earlier because of the storm. I went back to the hayloft.

"From that moment it was calm. Then one day, Antosia came and told me that my parents were alive. They were sending someone to fetch me. I thought that she wanted to get rid of me. But she said that my parents were in my mother's village. I could not sleep all night and beseeched God to let me reach them. Antosia had suffered a great deal because of me, because Danylo was afraid to hide me. She had spent two weeks in the hospital after he had hit her on the head. Despite this she kept taking care of me. She often said that if she were to send me away, she would dream about my mother and father. She was afraid of that and therefore kept me. She was very good to me, and her aunt helped her. The next day Bogdan took me to my mother's village. I was hiding under the hay. It was very cold. On the way Ukrainian militiamen stopped him. They looked inside the cart, but everything was covered with snow, and they didn't find me. I nearly died of fear and held my breath. Bogdan was cursing the Germans and the police and the Jews. I could no longer feel the tips of my fingers and toes. When we arrived, Oksana told me to sit by the fireplace and gave me hot soup. Then I went to the hayloft to my parents. I was very happy.

"We are now in Dmytro's hayloft. They say that the Russians will soon be here. Mama is pregnant and Father is worried. It is cold and the wind is howling. It's very cramped and we have to be quiet and still all day. I found a crack in the wall and can look out to the forest. I think that soon we will be free. Mama is sleeping on her side next to me. I can feel her large tummy with the baby inside touching mine. The sun is about to rise. I am very hungry.

"On Thursday, Mama had pains in her tummy. When it was dark Father took her to Dmytro's house. He told me to stay in the hayloft but late at night I came down and crossed the yard to Dmytro's house. Inside, Mama was on the bed and Oksana was sitting on the floor in front of her. Father was pacing around the room. Dmytro told me to sit next to the fireplace. Above the fireplace there was a big axe with a shiny blade and a carved handle. Mama was crying out and I wanted to be next to her, but Father said I should stay where I was. I fell asleep on the floor. When I woke up, I heard a baby crying. It was dawn and Dmytro said that we must go back to the hayloft. Oksana's twins were also crying. Mama was weak and could hardly climb the ladder. Father was holding the baby wrapped up in a blanket. Yesterday when Mama was feeding the baby, one of the stableboys walked into the barn. I almost died of fright. Then Dmytro walked into the barn and said, 'Mykhailo, who told you to come here? Don't you have any work to do?' At night Oksana brought us some cooked *kasza* and bread and sat with us for a while. She said that Dmytro was worried about the baby, that now we could all end up in trouble. After Oksana left Mama was weeping. She said we must name the baby. I said that we should call him David, so that he will bring the Messiah.

"Yesterday, Oksana said that the Russians will arrive in a few weeks. Mama said that little David is not putting on weight. She doesn't have enough milk for him. I sometimes think it would be better not to have him. Then I feel guilty and worry that God will punish me for such thoughts. We are all full of lice now. A few days ago, it became warmer, and everything was wet in the hayloft. When David cries, Mama hugs him very tightly until he stops. Mama says that before the war Father read all the time. Now he has nothing to read and that makes him anxious. I want to write every day, but my pencil is getting shorter and I'm afraid of asking Oksana for another. Father says that today is Friday. I remember how Mama used to light the candles. It is dark and cold now. I will go to sleep and try to dream about that.

"Today is Purim. In school we always put on costumes. Once we did a play called *Joseph and his Brothers*, and I was an angel and had wings. Dmytro told Father that the Russians bombed our city. I was happy. Oksana told me that the Germans were looking for food in the villages and if they came here, they would search the hayloft. I was very scared.

"Last week was terrible. The Germans moved into the village. They are everywhere. Father says that they are in the Grafina's villa. We hear their trucks all day. Oksana could not bring us food. There are always soldiers walking around. My body aches all over because I cannot move. Dmytro told Father that the gymnasium in Zaklots was on fire and people could smell the smoke in the nearby villages. We can hear airplanes every day.

"This morning Dmytro told Father that Zaklots was liberated by the Russians. They must be here soon. We are very happy. Oksana made us *pierogi* with cheese. I pray that we will celebrate Passover next week in freedom.

"This morning I woke up very early because I heard a noise outside. Father and Mama are sleeping. Mama is holding David to her breast. It is very stuffy in the hayloft. I am itching all over from the lice. I looked out through the crack. A big truck came from the village. The Germans were shouting. Then they got into their automobiles and drove away. I couldn't believe my eyes. I stood on a haystack and opened the hatch in the ceiling. The cold air made me gasp. The darkness was lifting. There was not a cloud in the sky. It was very still and quiet. A large butterfly flew up toward me and I was jealous of it for being so free when I am locked inside. Now I will go back to sleep and write more later. I am very hungry. But soon we will be free."

OLD BERMAN

I had to wait for the semester to end transcribe and translate Judit's notebook. In June 2019, I sent the translation to Tali, saying that if she liked, she could send it on to Andriy. I wanted to add, "Now he will be able to see how his grandfather cut short a life so full of hope despite everything she had experienced, just moments before she might have been liberated." But there was no point to it. "This story is over," I wrote. "We were all sucked into it and now we know everything that can be known, which amounts to very little. I feel very empty right now, very alone, on this vast continent which I have made my home. Perhaps I know more than I should. Or perhaps I still know nothing." I wished her good luck with her new life in New Zealand and went for a long walk around the lake next to my home. It was a glorious summer day and it occurred to me that as we get older, we are increasingly grateful for every such gift from nature as we count down how many such days we have left.

That night, I was rummaging through my papers and found the drafts for a story I had begun writing in the 1980s, while staying at a friend's apartment in Hampstead. It was prompted by a comment my mother had made to me when she and my father came to celebrate

Passover with me in my one-room lodging in Oxford. I had only written the first few pages and then abandoned it, having decided to dedicate myself only to my studies. It was about my great-great grandfather's death. Reading it after all those years, I realized that I had set out on this quest long before I knew it.

Old Berman had a very long life. He also chose a good moment to die. Or at least as good as one could choose at that time. People said he was 96 or 97 years old. Others insisted he was a 103. He had been old for a long time, and had raised two families, his own children and then his grandchildren, Renczi, Szymen, Chaim, and Ovadia, who were still small when their father, his son, died. Many decades later his great-granddaughter, my mother, still remembered him sitting on the steps of his house in the village of Vozhnor on the Czeremosz on sunny days, warming his bones and wrapped in thought. Every once in a while, he'd wave his hand in front of his face and mutter, "Arop fun mark, enough with that," as if some lingering memory was hovering around him like a bothersome fly.

He had many memories, of course, but they were all jumbled together, confusing each other, making less and less sense. They surfaced from his mind like pages torn out of an old novel, without beginning or end and entirely irrelevant to anything that was happening around him. After all, he had been born even before the old Kaiser Franz Joseph had come to the throne. All that has happened since! How people have changed! The rivers of blood, the dynasties turned into dust, the armies now resting in their graves, the endless occupations and liberations, the flags and the songs, the sorrows and lamentations, who could make sense of it all?

The day old Berman died, in early summer of 1937, his whole family gathered around him. It was a large family, spanning many generations. He took his time to die, despite his age. For two weeks— or that is what people subsequently said, and very few reliable witnesses were left to remember that event after all that came later— they traveled from across the province. They came by train and bus, by cart and on horseback, on foot and even, in one rare case, with their very own automobile. Not everyone could come. His beloved Renczi and her three children and husband had gone to Palestine, and Szymen had gone to America, but ended up in Paraguay, from which he had sent a lovely photo of himself dressed in a three-piece suit. But everyone else was there.

It was a good time to gather the family; many of them never met again, and within a few years almost all of them were dead, the young and the old, strewn in ravines and forests, buried in shallow mass graves, or turned into ashes used to fertilize the ground surrounding the gas chambers where they had been murdered. They died in fear and horror, hungry, hunted down like animals, having first lost their loved ones, often in front of their eyes, having been betrayed by their neighbors, demeaned by their occupiers, humiliated and dehumanized until the moment they drew their last breath. It was a good time to meet in 1937 when old Berman died, because everyone was still alive, and no one could imagine what the future had in store for them, not even the most pessimistic among them. Pessimism, as they used to joke, was the only realistic way to ponder the future. But in retrospect even the bleakest premonitions appeared too rosy.

And so they all came to that village on the banks of the Czeremosz that separated Poland and Romania. There were Renczi's other two brothers, Chaim the violinist, who was still remembered decades later for the sweet tunes he played at family gatherings, and the other brother, Ovadia, whose wife, curiously, had the same name as Chaim's. But he had no children, whereas Chaim had been blessed with two. Both brothers had moved out of the village to Vosok on the eastern slopes of the Carpathians, a beautiful little town where skiers would gather before heading off to the snowy peaks in the West, as they still do today. Did the two families travel together to see old Berman for the last time? What did they talk about on the way? Did the wives, Chaim's Raisel and Ovadia's Raisel, get along with each other? Were the two brothers saddened by the death of their grandfather, who had cared for them during their childhood? Were they glad to meet the rest of the family and to spend a few days back in their ancestral village, where they recalled eating *mamaliga* with fish as they played by the river?

Why did these two brothers not leave? Why did they stay in their little picturesque town, surrounded by forests and mountains and rivers, a small Jewish community in a sea of Ukrainians? They stayed. And later, like everyone else, they, their wives, and their children, were murdered. But in 1937, when they traveled to their grandfather's funeral, all that was still in the future and the sorrow at the death of the venerable old man was mixed with the joy of a family gathering.

Then there were my mother's uncles and aunt on her father's side. His only sister Rochaleh, the jewel in the crown, had married Max, a man with an academic degree. Her father, old Szumer, the famous Grafina's estate manager in Mierzyn, did not approve of the marriage. "What would the young couple live on?" he growled. "Would they fry the groom's diploma in goose fat for dinner?"

He set up his son-in-law to manage one of his mills, powered by the stream that wound its way through Zaklots, the town of my mother's childhood, to which the peasants would bring their wheat to be ground into flour. But it was the sturdy daughter of old Szumer's strapping clan that ran the business, while her scholarly husband sat in the corner reading books and magazines, perpetually bemoaning the meager holdings of Zaklots's proud library. If only he could travel to Lwów, he'd say, there, he nostalgically recalled, one could stroll through libraries all day long, and in the afternoons take coffee in one of the elegant cafés, well supplied with newspapers from around the world. At the time of old Berman's death, the couple already had a daughter, little Judit, but the baby, which one pernicious rumor later said had led to their dreadful end in the family's ancestral village, had not yet been conceived.

For my grandfather Yakov, who had fond memories of the sister he never saw again after going to Palestine, his own daughter was the true jewel in the crown, for she not only married an intellectual but became a scholar herself. He was not overly concerned with what kinds of degrees she had earned in Jerusalem and Los Angeles and New York. What mattered was that his daughter was an educated woman, unlike his two sons, who continued in their own way the family tradition of physical labor. They were tall, broad-shouldered, and good-natured men, not exceptionally bright and irretrievably innocent to the ways of the world. She was the apple of his eye. He could not know that his sister's jewel shone less and less brightly in the years following his departure, dulled by hard work and disillusionment. He never found out how her life was snuffed out on that chilly spring day in their childhood village, even though he spent much of his later years reading the gruesome accounts that filled the pages of communal memorial books.

"There were others," my mother said, "but I don't know their names." By the time I finally asked her, she was the only person alive with clear memories of that time. But she was not at that funeral, nor were her parents and two brothers. Only Hannaleh, my great-uncle Adolf's daughter, always wanted to go back there, though she had almost no memories of her own of the place, only the stories told by her mother. In any case, as my father used to say, she was not quite right in the head, and one could not trust her to distinguish reality from fantasy. And whenever he told her, "Hannaleh, there is nothing there for you, everyone's been murdered, there are only Ukrainians there now," she would look at him with such bewilderment and disbelief that all his resolve would dissipate, and he would change the subject. She never went there. In fact, the only member of my family who ever went back—but, of course, I never went back in the proper sense, because I had never been there before—was me.

My great-great-grandfather waited until everyone had arrived. It appears that in those days, before the catastrophe, people could choose the hour of their death. Not the day or the year, of course—because that might mean that no one would ever die, and people died then just as they die now—but the right moment. Soon thereafter the very notion of such a moment was eradicated in a blizzard of shrieks and obscenities, horror and incredulity, blood and pain and eventual resignation and indifference. Death came in so many new ways that one could never prepare for it as one had done in those recent, distant years. In 1937, old Berman waited patiently, dozing off, muttering some prayers, sipping tiny portions of chicken broth, recalling his own youth and vigor, the hardships of poverty and the joys of love and family, community and faith. But in truth, we know very little about old Berman, and of the thoughts that he kept brushing off like a troublesome fly when he sat on the porch and warmed his bones in the gentle sun, so different from the merciless ball of fire his granddaughter encountered when she set foot on the shores of the Promised Land.

She did not know what happened to them. But we must imagine it. We cannot let them die as if they just vanished into thin air. Their deaths were not a puff of smoke, a mysterious heavenly act, a stroke of bad luck; the earth did not open up and swallow them. We may not know precisely how they died, and some might say it is inappropriate to imagine it. But we know how many, so many others, did die. And so, we must tell the story of their deaths as if we know, on the basis of scant information, rumors and tales, because we must not allow for these deaths, dreadful as they were, to be marshalled into the ranks of martyrdom and obscurity, obfuscation and shame. They died as they lived, as human beings, murdered by others just like them, in fear and terror and pain. And although countless others died in similar ways, each death was unique, and each soul trembled for itself, alone in an ocean of horror.

In February 2020, just as the first news of the pandemic was beginning to filter through, I had a last communication from Tali. She did not move in with her Italian friend Massimo in New Zealand after all. She was writing from Lviv, where Andriy was spending his Sabbatical year. They were living together. For the next few months, I assumed that the pandemic had made it impossible for them to leave. Perhaps, I thought, they would stay together in Galicia, where we all once came from. Her last words to me were, "I've finally come home." That was what her mother had wanted. But I was skeptical. After all those years of wandering, would Tali be able to stay in that land of buried memories and unmarked mass graves? But we lost touch.

Then history came back, and Russia invaded Ukraine. Now even the dead could not rest in peace. I was anxious to hear from Tali, but no word came. A friend wrote me from Israel that her son, a paramedic who volunteered to help refugees, had apparently seen Tali in Przemyśl, astride the Polish-Ukrainian border, caring for evacuated Ukrainian orphans. Did Andriy go to fight to save Ukraine, to make his grandfather proud? The world had turned around again, and once more, millions of people were losing their homes, entire cities were in ruins. At least she tried, I thought.

ACKNOWLEDGMENTS

I would like to offer heartfelt thanks to Stephen Durrant, Sofia Grachova, David Haig, Hannan Hever, Daniel Lieberman, Frances Tanzer, and Bernhard Widdig, for reading drafts of this book and offering critical comments and suggestions that vastly improved it. Thank you to Eileen Chow, for giving me the opportunity to speak about it for the first time in a public forum at Duke University. I am grateful to Liesbeth Heenk, without whom this book would not have seen the light of day, and for the excellent copy editing that greatly facilitated its readability. My daughter, Shira Li Bartov, offered many striking personal and literary insights. As always, my wife, Wai-yee Li, spent more time than anyone should on reading, correcting, and discussing every element of this book with me. I doubt that I would have been able to set out on this journey, let alone complete it, without her sage advice, and mere presence.

AMSTERDAM PUBLISHERS HOLOCAUST LIBRARY

The series **Holocaust Survivor Memoirs World War II** consists of the following autobiographies of survivors:

Outcry. Holocaust Memoirs, by Manny Steinberg

Hank Brodt Holocaust Memoirs. A Candle and a Promise, by Deborah Donnelly

The Dead Years. Holocaust Memoirs, by Joseph Schupack

Rescued from the Ashes. The Diary of Leokadia Schmidt, Survivor of the Warsaw Ghetto, by Leokadia Schmidt

My Lvov. Holocaust Memoir of a twelve-year-old Girl, by Janina Hescheles

Remembering Ravensbrück. From Holocaust to Healing, by Natalie Hess

Wolf. A Story of Hate, by Zeev Scheinwald with Ella Scheinwald

Save my Children. An Astonishing Tale of Survival and its Unlikely Hero, by Leon Kleiner with Edwin Stepp

Holocaust Memoirs of a Bergen-Belsen Survivor & Classmate of Anne Frank, by Nanette Blitz Konig

Defiant German - Defiant Jew. A Holocaust Memoir from inside the Third Reich, by Walter Leopold with Les Leopold

In a Land of Forest and Darkness. The Holocaust Story of two Jewish Partisans, by Sara Lustigman Omelinski

Holocaust Memories. Annihilation and Survival in Slovakia, by Paul
Davidovits

From Auschwitz with Love. The Inspiring Memoir of Two Sisters'
Survival, Devotion and Triumph Told by Manci Grunberger Beran & Ruth
Grunberger Mermelstein, by Daniel Seymour

Remetz. Resistance Fighter and Survivor of the Warsaw Ghetto, by Jan
Yohay Remetz

My March Through Hell. A Young Girl's Terrifying Journey to Survival,
by Halina Kleiner with Edwin Stepp

The series **Holocaust Survivor True Stories WWII** consists of the
following biographies:

Among the Reeds. The true story of how a family survived the Holocaust,
by Tammy Bottner

A Holocaust Memoir of Love & Resilience. Mama's Survival from
Lithuania to America, by Ettie Zilber

Living among the Dead. My Grandmother's Holocaust Survival Story of
Love and Strength, by Adena Bernstein Astrowsky

Heart Songs. A Holocaust Memoir, by Barbara Gilford

Shoes of the Shoah. The Tomorrow of Yesterday, by Dorothy Pierce

Hidden in Berlin. A Holocaust Memoir, by Evelyn Joseph Grossman

Separated Together. The Incredible True WWII Story of Soulmates
Stranded an Ocean Apart, by Kenneth P. Price, Ph.D.

The Man Across the River. The incredible story of one man's will to survive the Holocaust, by Zvi Wiesenfeld

If Anyone Calls, Tell Them I Died. A Memoir, by Emanuel (Manu) Rosen

The House on Thrömerstrasse. A Story of Rebirth and Renewal in the Wake of the Holocaust, by Ron Vincent

Dancing with my Father. His hidden past. Her quest for truth. How Nazi Vienna shaped a family's identity, by Jo Sorochinsky

The Story Keeper. Weaving the Threads of Time and Memory - A Memoir, by Fred Feldman

Krisia's Silence. The Girl who was not on Schindler's List, by Ronny Hein

Defying Death on the Danube. A Holocaust Survival Story, by Debbie J. Callahan with Henry Stern

A Doorway to Heroism. A decorated German-Jewish Soldier who became an American Hero, by Rabbi W. Jack Romberg

The Shoemaker's Son. The Life of a Holocaust Resister, by Laura Beth Bakst

The Redhead of Auschwitz. A True Story, by Nechama Birnbaum

Land of Many Bridges. My Father's Story, by Bela Ruth Samuel Tenenholtz

Creating Beauty from the Abyss. The Amazing Story of Sam Herciger, Auschwitz Survivor and Artist, by Lesley Ann Richardson

On Sunny Days We Sang. A Holocaust Story of Survival and Resilience, by Jeannette Grunhaus de Gelman

Painful Joy. A Holocaust Family Memoir, by Max J. Friedman

I Give You My Heart. A True Story of Courage and Survival, by Wendy Holden

In the Time of Madmen, by Mark A. Prelas

Monsters and Miracles. Horror, Heroes and the Holocaust, by Ira Wesley Kitmacher

Flower of Vlora. Growing up Jewish in Communist Albania, by Anna Kohen

Aftermath: Coming of Age on Three Continents. A Memoir, by Annette Libeskind Berkovits

Not a real Enemy. The True Story of a Hungarian Jewish Man's Fight for Freedom, by Robert Wolf

Zaidy's War. Four Armies, Three Continents, Two Brothers. One Man's Impossible Story of Endurance, by Martin Bodek

The Glassmaker's Son. Looking for the World my Father left behind in Nazi Germany, by Peter Kupfer

The Apprentice of Buchenwald. The True Story of the Teenage Boy Who Sabotaged Hitler's War Machine, by Oren Schneider

---

The series **Jewish Children in the Holocaust** consists of the following autobiographies of Jewish children hidden during WWII in the Netherlands:

Searching for Home. The Impact of WWII on a Hidden Child, by Joseph Gosler

See You Tonight and Promise to be a Good Boy! War memories, by Salo Muller

Sounds from Silence. Reflections of a Child Holocaust Survivor, Psychiatrist and Teacher, by Robert Krell

Sabine's Odyssey. A Hidden Child and her Dutch Rescuers, by Agnes Schipper

The Journey of a Hidden Child, by Harry Pila and Robin Black

––––––––

The series **New Jewish Fiction** consists of the following novels, written by Jewish authors. All novels are set in the time during or after the Holocaust.

The Corset Maker. A Novel, by Annette Libeskind Berkovits

Escaping the Whale. The Holocaust is over. But is it ever over for the next generation? by Ruth Rotkowitz

When the Music Stopped. Willy Rosen's Holocaust, by Casey Hayes

Hands of Gold. One Man's Quest to Find the Silver Lining in Misfortune, by Roni Robbins

The Girl Who Counted Numbers. A Novel, by Roslyn Bernstein

There was a garden in Nuremberg. A Novel, by Navina Michal Clemerson

The Butterfly and the Axe, by Omer Bartov

Good for a Single Journey, by Helen Joyce

––––––––

The series **Holocaust Heritage** consists of the following memoirs by 2G:

The Cello Still Sings. A Generational Story of the Holocaust and of the Transformative Power of Music, by Janet Horvath

---

The series **Holocaust Books for Young Adults** consists of the following novels, based on true stories:

The Boy behind the Door. How Salomon Kool Escaped the Nazis. Inspired by a True Story, by David Tabatsky

Running for Shelter. A True Story, by Suzette Sheft

The Precious Few. An Inspirational Saga of Courage based on True Stories, by David Twain with Art Twain

Jacob's Courage: A Holocaust Love Story, by Charles S. Weinblatt

---

The series **WW2 Historical Fiction** consists of the following novels, some of which are based on true stories:

Mendelevski's Box. A Heartwarming and Heartbreaking Jewish Survivor's Story, by Roger Swindells

A Quiet Genocide. The Untold Holocaust of Disabled Children WW2 Germany, by Glenn Bryant

The Knife-Edge Path, by Patrick T. Leahy

Brave Face. The Inspiring WWII Memoir of a Dutch/German Child, by I. Caroline Crocker and Meta A. Evenbly

When We Had Wings. The Gripping Story of an Orphan in Janusz Korczak's Orphanage. A Historical Novel, by Tami Shem-Tov

Want to be an AP book reviewer?

Reviews are very important in a world dominated by the social media and social proof. Please drop us a line if you want to join the *AP review team*. We will then add you to our list of advance reviewers. No strings attached. info@amsterdampublishers.com

Made in the USA
Las Vegas, NV
29 January 2024

85057625R00121